Teaching Engineering Made Easy 2
Another Friendly Introduction to Engineering Activities for Middle School Teachers (Second Edition)

by Celeste Baine, Cathi Cox-Boniol and Elizabeth Parry

Engineering Education
Service Center

Eugene, OR

Teaching Engineering Made Easy 2
Another Friendly Introduction to Engineering Activities for Middle School Teachers (Second Edition)
By Celeste Baine, Cathi Cox-Boniol and Elizabeth Parry

Published by:
  Bonamy Publishing
  1004 5th Street
  Springfield, OR 97477 U.S.A.
  (541) 988-1005
  www.engineeringedu.com

Printed in the United States of America

Teaching Engineering Made Easy 2: Another Friendly Introduction to Engineering Activities for Middle School Teachers (Second Edition)

ISBN 13: 978-0-9819300-5-3

How to Order:
Single copies may be ordered from:
Engineering Education Service Center,
1004 5th Street, Springfield, OR 97477;
Telephone (541) 988-1005

CIP Pending

This book is dedicated to Terry. Without your encouragement, I wouldn't be doing this great work.

-Celeste Baine

Contents

What you can do with this book...

Teaching Engineering Made Easy 2 gives classroom teachers a unique, easy and dynamic way to enhance any engineering lessons and meet curriculum standards and competencies. You'll find lessons and activities that actively engage students in learning about engineering and our technological world while applying creativity and innovation to complete the projects.

Developed to help middle and high school teachers teach engineering, this easy and exciting, time and work saving book can be used in the classroom, an informal science environment, to enhance an event or competition, at an engineering camp or any other educational setting. Each section offers detailed lessons with reproducible student activity sheets.

Filled with innovative tools, dynamic activities and practical lesson plans, *Teaching Engineering Made Easy 2* continues where Volume One left off, with all new activities that will supercharge the teaching of engineering principles, biomedical and electrical engineering. Students will find that engineering is not something to be afraid of but a realistic way to solve the problems of everyday life.

For easy use, the lessons and activities are bound to enable an 8 ½" x 11" lay-flat format for photocopying.

This book is organized into 3 sections:
    1. Teaching Engineering
    2. Engineering Activities
       a. Team Building Activities
       b. Engineering Principles Activities
       c. Biomedical Engineering Activities
       d. Electrical Engineering Activities
    3. Engineering Puzzles

Each section offers detailed lessons with reproducible student activity sheets. Each lesson can include:
    • Standards alignment
    • Overview/Objective
    • Background information
    • Teacher notes
    • Safety notes
    • A list of materials needed to complete the activity
    • An easy-to-follow procedure for presenting the lesson
    • Student sheets

Learning Experience	Skills and Main Concepts Developed in Each Learning Experience
1. Engineering IceBreaker	Communication, investigating, observing, problem solving
2. Find Someone Who	Communication, investigating, observing, problem solving
3. I Spy Engineering	Communication, critical thinking, predicting, inferring
4. You Might Be An Engineer If...	Critical thinking, communication, observing
5. The World Stops Without Engineers	Research, investigating, critical thinking, communication
6. Measure It!	Critical thinking, problem solving, experimenting, measuring, observing, investigating, redesigning, testing, product design
7. Born to Rock!	Critical thinking, problem solving, observing, measurement, product design, communication
8. Forces - Compression and Tension	Critical thinking, problem solving, observing, measurement, compression, tension, investigating, communication
9. Tsunami Shelter Platform	Critical thinking, problem solving, observing, measurement, product design, communication
10. Paper Airplane	Critical thinking, problem solving, observing, measurement, product design, communication
11 Boning Up On Bones	Critical thinking, observing, predicting, investigating, mass measurement, procedure design, communication, forces
12. Keep it Moving	Problem solving, procedure design, predicting, inferring, observing, investigating, physical/chemical properties
13. Prosthetic Hand	Critical thinking, problem solving, observing, measurement, product design, communication
14. Gut Reaction	Observing, investigating, acids/bases/pH, solutions, chemical reactions, chemical formulas, catalysts, reaction rates
15. Protect Your Melon	Observing, inferring, measurement, experimental design, investigating, motion, communication, critical thinking, problem solving
16. Bright Light	Measurement, collecting and organizing data, graphing, graphical analysis, experimental design, investigating, variables
17. Putting it to the Test	Observing, critical thinking, problem solving, investigating, electrical conductors and insulators, circuit design, communication
18. Spider Circuits	Observing, critical thinking, problem solving, investigating, electrical conductors and insulators, circuit design, communication
19. Amplified Kazoo	Observing, measuring, soldering, critical thinking, problem solving, investigating, circuit design, testing
20. Lunar Treasures	Critical thinking, problem solving, experimenting, measuring, observing, investigating, electrical conductors and insulators, circuit design, product design

Engineers Change the World

Engineering is a very humanistic field because the creations of engineers are all about making life better, easier, less expensive or more fun. It is one of the most progressive, challenging, creative and rewarding fields that can be studied today. Engineers improve the environment, protect rare or exotic animals, explore other galaxies, help ease world hunger, investigate cures for cancer, work in fashion and so much more.

Ivar Sanders, the inventor of the Nokia router (a device that allows cell phone towers to connect to each other) says that engineers are artists with a practical twist. They use their creativity and knowledge to see products and applications for things that haven't yet been created, and turn their thoughts of "what if" into realities of the future.

Engineering is the second largest profession in the nation with more than 2.3 million engineers in the workforce. They may design products such as automobiles or design infrastructures such as the roads, bridges, structures, and streets the automobiles travel on. They may work to make our environment cleaner or reduce hunger around the world. They may work in entertainment designing rides for theme parks, better shopping experiences in malls or they may develop better communication systems. You can also find engineers working for the biggest cosmetics companies making cosmetics safer, or the biggest food companies making food healthier with better flavor. There is almost nothing that engineers don't have a hand designing.

The majority of all technological advances, such as HDTV, wearable computers, the Internet, the Mars Rover, and artificial joints, heart values and prosthetics (titanium knees and hips), can be attributed to the work of engineers. Prestige and a high income are also part of an engineer's job satisfaction. Because of their skills, training and the work they do, engineers are committed to being life-long learners.

A degree in engineering can open many doors.

Not all people who graduate as engineers work in the field. They may also:

- Continue their schooling to become attorneys, doctors, entrepreneurs, teachers, writers and even politicians

- Improve society by developing green technologies or solutions for sustainable living

- Reduce pollution

- Ease world hunger

- Invent exciting cutting-edge technology such as new forms of transportation, medical devices or pocket-sized electronics

- Make life more convenient, cheaper, easier or more fun, and

- Develop new theories to change the ways we think about the world.

Students who have the drive to complete an engineering degree will have completed courses in math, science, English and social studies and therefore could become one of the most valuable types of engineers – one who can communicate the language of engineering to other non-technical persons through excellent verbal and written skills.

The world needs all kinds of engineers and, with a solid foundation provided by an engineering degree, a career in engineering can take you anywhere you want to go.

Teaching Engineering

Engineering is problem-solving. Many teachers enjoy teaching engineering because it combines math, science, language arts, social studies, team building and creativity with a practical twist. Students learn to work together, increase their communication skills, and enhance their presentation abilities by demonstrating and discussing design strategies with the rest of the class.

Students enjoy using the skills and knowledge they have gained abstractly. Engineering projects offer a great venue for students to show themselves and others that they can:

- Manage time and projects
- Study a situation or problem critically
- Research relevant information
- Problem solve
- Use a logical process to plan solutions
- Fail, and learn from it
- Talk intelligently about what they've done, and how they did it

Hands-on activities and project-based learning are fun and effective ways to help students learn and retain more math and science concepts. By choosing to teach engineering, teachers can help students make the links between classroom learning, their everyday lives and the wider world. Project based learning can help students visualize abstract science and math concepts. Using hands-on activities, engineering design serves as the bridge to bring color to math and science concepts. This bridge makes our designed world more understandable, relevant and fun.

By promoting engineering as a viable career option, teachers also:

1. Help provide a stronger workforce in all fields of Science, Technology, Engineering and Math (STEM).
2. Help create a technologically literate people and society.
3. Provide students with the skills they will need to thrive in a technological society.

How engineering is presented to students can make the difference between them being interested or not. In the old days, educators described engineers as builders, operators, planners and maintainers.

Students today are more likely to respond well to a description of engineers as designers, creators or inventors (NAE, 2008).

More exciting messages include:

- Aerospace engineers explore the galaxy!
- Biomedical engineers help people live longer and more comfortably!
- Environmental engineers protect the planet!
- Agricultural engineers feed the world!
- Telecommunications engineers connect the world!

50 Reasons to Teach Engineering

This list could also be called, "50 Reasons to Become an Engineer." They work hand in hand. With a little creativity, any one of these reasons can become a lesson or discussion about engineering careers and serve as a catapult to further exploration.

1. To avert a fresh water shortage in 48 countries (2.8 billion people) by 2025.
2. To save the rainforests.
3. To design products and assistive technologies so aging people can maintain healthy, productive lifestyles.
4. To give the underserved a clear path to family wage careers.
5. To give students whose talents lie with the concrete rather than the abstract an avenue to success.
6. To make sure students who excel at abstract academics can make the transition to concrete applications and specific problem-solving.
7. To give women another venue for success.
8. To enlighten students who don't know what engineering is about.
9. To save rare or exotic animals from extinction.
10. To educate a potential President of the United States.
11. To help the energy crisis by finding new ways to produce or store solar, wind, wave, geothermal and other sources of energy.
12. To find ways to make nuclear waste non-toxic.
13. To develop safe nuclear energy.
14. To help find a cure for AIDS.
15. To help develop new medicines for numerous diseases.
16. To invent smaller, more affordable computers.
17. To make better theme parks and safer roller coasters.
18. To keep up with the technology needs of society.
19. To help the U.S. retain its position as a world power.
20. To give students the tools they need for their futures.
21. To reverse engineer the brain.
22. To counter the violence of terrorists.
23. To improve methods of instruction and learning.
24. To create better virtual reality systems.
25. To capture carbon dioxide.
26. To sustain the infrastructure of cities and living spaces.
27. To explore other galaxies.
28. To understand more about our planet.
29. To reduce our vulnerability to assaults in cyberspace.
30. To prevent devastation from hurricanes and other natural disasters.
31. To improve transportation on land, sea and air.
32. To improve our connectivity and ability to communicate with family and friends.

33. To help us save money on everything.

34. To keep us safe at home and in other countries.

35. To lessen our vulnerability to disease.

36. To improve the quality of the air we breathe.

37. To help our pets live longer.

38. To aid veterinarians in caring for animals.

39. To make food taste better.

40. To make food better for our health.

41. To prevent car accidents with better traffic infrastructure.

42. To create greener buildings and systems that minimize our impact on the Earth.

43. To understand the oceans and their ability to help us.

44. To reduce the impact of war.

45. To lessen the need for war.

46. To enhance the beauty of our surroundings.

47. To have better furniture and computer peripherals that reduce our risk of carpal tunnel or back pain.

48. To save the polar bears and other endangered species.

49. To get more people where they need to go quickly, safely and conveniently.

50. To decrease the incidence of disease and famine.

The list above can also be used to assign students the task of preparing a report about how engineers are involved in creating a solution for each.

Information Overload

There are hundreds of organizations and colleges that are producing materials to educate students about engineering careers. There is so much information, it's difficult to shake out which are the most valuable in serving your educational problem or need. When surfing the web, it's easy to get overwhelmed with all the websites, portals and videos on YouTube that tout engineering.

As recently as 25 years ago, we lived in a time of content scarcity. If we wanted to research something, we went to the library. If we wanted to watch a cartoon, we got up early on Saturday morning. If we wanted to listen to a new song, we waited for the radio to play it again.

Today, kids live in a world of content infinity. When they have a question, they ask Google, Ask.com or Wikipedia. When they want to watch a specific cartoon, they push the "play" button on their on-demand system or they visit the channel's website to watch it on the Internet. When they hear a song they like, they download it from iTunes. They live in a world of made-to-order instant gratification.

For educators, the problem isn't about finding information on engineering careers, locating hands-on activities, or helping students decide which college to attend. It's more about figuring out:

- What is appealing to students (what drives this generation),

- Getting that tailored information to them (books, DVDs, hands-on projects, posters, websites or whatever), and

- Answering the questions that they haven't even thought to ask yet (Will I like engineering? How hard will I have to work?, Is it worth the hard work?, etc.).

Updating the Dialog

The National Academy of Engineering (NAE) conducted a major study to address the messages we convey to pre-college students about engineering. The findings (NAE, 2008) show that young people want jobs that make a difference.

Additional recommendations from the research study are as follows:

- Stop reinforcing the images of 'nerdy and boring'.
- Stop focusing on math and science as the needed inputs, and instead focus on the outputs, career opportunities, and making a difference in the world.
- Use the word 'create' not 'build'.
- Use images of people, not things: especially avoid using gears and mechanical-looking things.
- Use the following five words to describe engineering: discovery, design, imagination, innovation, contribution.
- Describe engineers as creative problem solvers, essential to health, happiness and safety.
- Emphasize that engineers shape the future.

The recommendations above require that you update your terminology when talking about engineering. Learning a new form of communication is like learning a new language. It takes patience and practice before it sounds and feels right. The important thing is that you keep trying.

Engineering and Personality

It's important to help students choose a career that is compatible with their personality. Encourage them to find out as much about themselves as possible by:

1. Taking personality assessments at career guidance centers.
2. Talking to their friends, family, guidance counselors, math and science teachers to learn others' perceptions about who they are or what they want.
3. Writing down a description of their perfect job.
4. Writing down their strengths and weaknesses.
5. Thinking about why a certain job is a good fit for their personality or interests.

Have your students check the want ads to see what employers expect, and push them to contact a local college of engineering to see if it offers tours or programs for middle or high school students. For most students, contacting schools or companies will be out of their comfort zone. You may have better success by arranging field trips to colleges or local engineering facilities. Getting parental support is also a great way to manage the situation. You may find that by talking to parents about company or college tours, they'll know of resources or opportunities that you didn't know were available.

Career placement and counseling centers offer the Myers-Briggs Type Indicator®, a primary assessment tool that may give students some insight into who they are, what conditions they may prefer at work, and how they think about things. The test is designed to provide insight on how their interests match up with the interests of others in a particular occupation. However, it should be noted that the assessment, although great for self-discovery, is just an indicator and cannot predict whether or not the student will succeed in the occupation indicated, or be a good engineer.

There is no one "right" personality for a career in engineering. Engineers can be:

- Extrovert or introvert.
- Someone who thrives on change, challenge, consistency or adversity.
- Leaders or a member of a team.
- Hard workers and lifetime learners.
- Good under pressure, decision makers and effective communicators.

If students feel it is a good personality fit, and are willing to put forth the effort to not only excel in math and science, but language arts and social studies too, then engineering has abundant opportunities. The engineering profession needs and consists of all types of engineers.

When helping students to consider a career in engineering, let them know that it will be a lifelong learning experience; and everything they do to prepare for it will help them reach their intended goal. The more you help expose students to the world of engineering, the more opportunities they can explore.

Team Building Activities

Engineering Career Icebreaker
Jumping into engineering

Time Required: 10-15 minutes

How this Learning Experience Meets the National Science Education Standards:
As a result of activities in grades 5-8, all students should develop:

Content Standard A: Science as Inquiry
Abilities Necessary to Do Scientific Inquiry
- Use appropriate tools and techniques to gather, analyze and interpret data
- Think critically and logically to make the relationships between evidence and explanations.
- Recognize and analyze alternative explanations and predictions.

Content Standard G: History and Nature of Science
Science as a Human Endeavor
- Women and men of various social and ethnic backgrounds engage in activities of science, engineering, and related fields; some scientists work in teams, and some work alone, but all communicate extensively with others.
- Science requires different abilities, depending on such factors as the field and study and the type of inquiry.

Overview:

The objective of the following activity is for the members of the group to become better acquainted with the characteristics and backgrounds of their fellow members.

Safety Notes:

Attention should be given to maintaining an area clear of any obstacles that could pose a danger for the participants. Should the group include individuals with special needs, modifications or accommodations will need to be addressed so they are not at a disadvantage experientially.

Getting Started:

Copy the Engineering Career Ice Breaker sheet on the following page so that each student gets a copy

Materials Needed per Student:

- One pencil or pen
- One Engineering Career Ice Breaker sheet

Procedure:

1. Have the students assemble in the activity area.
2. Instruct the students that they will have 5 minutes to walk around the room and attempt to find someone who fits the description of the characteristics in each box. When they have found someone matching that description, that person writes his or her name in the respective box on the student's paper.
3. Award a prize to the student or students that finish first.
4. Facilitate a discussion that builds on the student responses.

Engineering Career Ice Breaker

Walk around the room and attempt to find someone who fits the description of the characteristics below. When you have found someone matching that description, that person writes his or her name in the respective box on your paper. You have five minutes to complete the activity.

The member with the most different names after five minutes is declared the winner!

Find someone who...

Has visited an engineering company	Father is an engineer	Favorite subject is math	Mother is an engineer	Is a member of a club
Has green eyes	Wants to go to college	Aunt or Uncle is an engineer	Wants to know more about engineering	Can juggle
Wants to be an engineer	Wants to design roller coasters	Loves to eat	Wears glasses	Has a 4.0 GPA
Has met someone famous	Can name 5 different types of engineering	Wants to be a millionaire	Rides his or her bike to school	Has a younger sister
Has visited a foreign country	Has taken apart something they couldn't put back together	Has invented something at home	Was born in a different state	Likes hard rock music

Find Someone Who

Engineering is Everywhere

Time Required: 45-60 minutes

How this Learning Experience Meets the National Science Education Standards:

As a result of activities in grades 5-8, all students should develop:

Content Standard A: Science as Inquiry
Abilities Necessary to Do Scientific Inquiry

- Use appropriate tools and techniques to gather, analyze and interpret data
- Think critically and logically to make the relationships between evidence and explanations.
- Recognize and analyze alternative explanations and predictions.

Content Standard G: History and Nature of Science
Science as a Human Endeavor

- Women and men of various social and ethnic backgrounds engage in activities of science, engineering, and related fields; some scientists work in teams, and some work alone, but all communicate extensively with others.
- Science requires different abilities, depending on such factors as the field and study and the type of inquiry.

Overview:

The objective of the following activity is for the members of the group to learn about engineering trivia, and integrate history and current events with careers in engineering. They will also become better acquainted with the characteristics and backgrounds of their fellow members.

Safety Notes:

Attention should be given to maintaining an area clear of any obstacles that could pose a danger for the participants. Should the group include individuals with special needs, modifications of accommodations will need to be addressed so they are not at a disadvantage experientially.

Getting Started:

Copy the "Find Someone Who" instructions on the following page so that each student gets a copy.

Materials Needed per Student:

- One pencil or pen
- One "Find Someone Who" sheet

Procedure:

1. Have the students assemble in the activity area.
2. Instruct the students that they will walk around the room and attempt to find someone who knows the answer to the questions on his or her "Find Someone Who" sheet. When they have found someone who knows the answer to one of the questions, that person writes his or her name and the answer after the question on the student's paper.
3. Award a prize to the student or students that finish first.
4. Facilitate a discussion that builds on the student responses.

Find Someone Who

Find someone in our group who knows the answer to each of the following items. You can only use each person's name once! Write down the answer and the name of the person who gave you the answer after each question. The first person to fill his or her sheet wins a FABULOUS prize!

1. An artificial big toe found on the foot of an Egyptian mummy is thought to be the world's earliest functioning prosthetic body part. What type of engineer is responsible for creating prosthetics such as knee and hip joints?

2. EPCOT's Land Pavilion probably employed an agricultural engineer to work in labs where they experiment with promising indoor farming techniques. In what resort area is EPCOT located?

3. Mechanical engineers are responsible for creating Olympic swimming pools that hold exactly one million gallons of water. Which American swimmer the most decorated Olympian of all time, with a total of 22 medals?

4. A chemical engineer was undoubtedly crucial in the production of this, the biggest selling soft drink in the world today.

5. The pride of civil engineers everywhere, this magnificent dam outside of Las Vegas is not only known as one of the greatest engineering works in history, it is said to have "transformed the American Southwest."

6. Some of the types of engineers who worked on creating NASA's *Curiosity* rover include: Aerospace, Electrical, Mechanical, Software, Robotic, Materials and Computer engineers. The rover *Curiosity* landed on what cosmic body, and began executing important experiments?

7. Computer engineers are largely responsible for our Internet website capabilities. In 2012, Facebook was the second most visited site on the Internet, what was the first?

8. The different contributions and works of environmental engineers can be celebrated and spotlighted during various events and programs on Earth Day each year. Where would you find Earth Day listed on the calendar?

9. Mechanical engineers design machines and motors, but Tom Scholz used his masters degree in mechanical engineering from MIT to lead this classic rock band whose hits include "More Than a Feeling," "Long Time" and "Amanda."

10. The work for manufacturing engineers was greatly enhanced with the improvement of the assembly line. And although it wasn't a new idea in 1913, it was tremendously improved by this man as he revolutionized the automobile industry.

11. When completing the DVD extras for "The Terminator," director James Cameron stated that he trained at the "Roger Corman Film School." But Corman, an industrial engineer turned filmmaker, couldn't have dreamed that his protégé would go on to direct the largest grossing movie of all time. What is it?

12. Transportation engineers were required to plan new traffic patterns when Houston's larger, more modern Reliant Stadium was erected to replace this 1965 site as the city's NFL venue.

13. Ocean engineers had their hands full when Mother Nature unleashed her wrath on the gulf coast with Hurricanes Katrina and Rita. In what year did this dual disaster occur?

14. This video game, designed by computer en ginners and released in 1985 was the first video game to sell 2 million cartridges.

15. Gaming and computer engineers are two types of engineers that create video games and hardware. In December 2009, what brand broke the record for best-selling console in a single month in the United States?

This page may be photocopied for use in the classroom.

Find Someone Who - Answer Sheet

Find someone in our group who knows the answer to each of the following items. You can only use each person's name once! Write down the answer and the name of the person who gave you the answer after each question. The first person to fill his or her sheet wins a FABULOUS prize!

1. An artificial big toe found on the foot of an Egyptian mummy is thought to be the world's earliest functioning prosthetic body part. What type of engineer is responsible for creating prosthetics such as knee and hip joints? ***Biomedical Engineers***

2. EPCOT's Land Pavilion probably employed an agricultural engineer to work in labs where they experiment with promising indoor farming techniques. In what resort area is EPCOT located? ***Disney World - Orlando, FL***

3. Mechanical engineers are responsible for creating Olympic swimming pools that hold exactly one million gallons of water. Which American swimmer the most decorated Olympian of all time, with a total of 22 medals? ***Michael Phelps***

4. A chemical engineer was undoubtedly crucial in the production of this, the biggest selling soft drink in the world today. ***Coca Cola Classic***

5. The pride of civil engineers everywhere, this magnificent dam outside of Las Vegas is not only known as one of the greatest engineering works in history, it is said to have "transformed the American Southwest." ***Hoover Dam***

6. Some of the types of engineers who worked on creating NASA's *Curiosity* rover include: Aerospace, Electrical, Mechanical, Software, Robotic, Materials and Computer engineers. The rover *Curiosity* landed on what cosmic body, and began executing important experiments? ***Mars***

7. Computer engineers are largely responsible for our Internet website capabilities. In 2012, Facebook was the second most visited site on the Internet, what was the first? ***Google***

8. The different contributions and works of environmental engineers can be celebrated and spotlighted during various events and programs on Earth Day each year. Where would you find Earth Day listed on the calendar? ***April 22***

9. Mechanical engineers design machines and motors, but Tom Scholz used his masters degree in ME from MIT to lead this classic rock band whose hits include "More Than a Feeling," "Long Time" and "Amanda." ***Boston***

10. The work for manufacturing engineers was greatly enhanced with the improvement of the assembly line. And although it wasn't a new idea in 1913, it was tremendously improved by this man as he revolutionized the automobile industry. ***Henry Ford***

11. When completing the DVD extras for "The Terminator," director James Cameron stated that he trained at the "Roger Corman Film School." But Corman, an industrial engineer turned filmmaker, couldn't have dreamed that his protégé would go on to direct the largest grossing movie of all time. What is it? ***Avatar***

12. Transportation engineers were required to plan new traffic patterns when Houston's larger, more modern Reliant Stadium was erected to replace this 1965 site as the city's NFL venue. ***Astrodome***

13. Ocean engineers had their hands full when Mother Nature unleashed her wrath on the gulf coast with Hurricanes Katrina and Rita. In what year did this dual disaster occur? ***2005***

14. This video game, designed by software engineers and released in 1985 was the first video game to sell 2 million cartridges. ***Space Invaders***

15. Gaming and computer engineers are two types of engineers that create video games and hardware. In December 2009, what brand broke the record for best-selling console in a single month in the United States? ***Wii***

I Spy Engineering

No spectacles required

Time Required: 10-15 minutes

How this Learning Experience Meets the National Science Education Standards:
As a result of activities in grades 5-8, all students should develop:

Content Standard A: Science as Inquiry
Abilities Necessary to Do Scientific Inquiry
- Use appropriate tools and techniques to gather, analyze and interpret data
- Think critically and logically to make the relationships between evidence and explanations.
- Recognize and analyze alternative explanations and predictions.

Content Standard G: History and Nature of Science
Science as a Human Endeavor
- Women and men of various social and ethnic backgrounds engage in activities of science, engineering, and related fields; some scientists work in teams, and some work alone, but all communicate extensively with others.
- Science requires different abilities, depending on such factors as the field and study and the type of inquiry.

Overview:

The objective of the following activity is for students to become more aware of engineering in their everyday lives.

Safety Notes:

Attention should be given to maintaining an area clear of any obstacles that could pose a danger for the participants. Should the group include individuals with special needs, modifications of accommodations will need to be addressed so they are not at a disadvantage experientially.

Getting Started:

Copy the "I Spy Engineering" sheet on the following page so that each team gets a copy.

Materials Needed:

- One pencil or pen per student
- One "I Spy Engineering" sheet per team

Procedure:

1. Have the students assemble in the activity area.
2. Instruct students to get into teams of two.
3. Give each team an "I Spy Engineering" sheet.
4. Tell the teams that they will have 2 minutes to write down everything they can see in the room, or out the window, that was designed or created by an engineer.
   Examples:
   - Chairs: Industrial, Mechanical, Chemical
   - Desks: Industrial, Mechanical, Chemical
   - Paint: Chemical
   - Flooring: Chemical
   - Lighting: Electrical
   - Pens/Pencils: Industrial, Chemical, Manufacturing
   - Tennis shoes: Sports Engineers (mechanical, biomedical, materials, and chemical)
   - Cell Phones: Electrical, Computer, Software, Materials
   - Computers: Electrical, Computer, Electronics, Software
4. Facilitate a discussion that builds on the student responses.

I Spy Engineering

Write down everything you can see in the room, or out the window, that was designed or created by an engineer. Examples: Chairs - Industrial, Mechanical, and/or Chemical Engineering; Paint - Chemical Engineering; Lighting - Electrical Engineering.

The person or team that sees the most items wins!

_____   _____

_____   _____

_____   _____

_____   _____

_____   _____

_____   _____

_____   _____

_____   _____

_____   _____

_____   _____

_____   _____

_____   _____

_____   _____

You Might Be An Engineer If:

Creating Cooperative Groups

Time Required: 30-45 minutes

How this Learning Experience Meets the National Science Education Standards:
As a result of activities in grades 5-8, all students should develop:

Content Standard A: Science as Inquiry
Abilities Necessary to Do Scientific Inquiry
- Use appropriate tools and techniques to gather, analyze and interpret data
- Think critically and logically to make the relationships between evidence and explanations.
- Recognize and analyze alternative explanations and predictions.

Content Standard G: History and Nature of Science
Science as a Human Endeavor
- Women and men of various social and ethnic backgrounds engage in activities of science, engineering, and related fields; some scientists work in teams, and some work alone, but all communicate extensively with others.
- Science requires different abilities, depending on such factors as the field and study and the type of inquiry.

Overview:

This activity is designed to effectively manage the transition from a whole group setting into a smaller cooperative group arrangement.

Teacher Notes:

Each of the phrases used in this experience correlate to some component of the content that will be addressed throughout the learning sequences.

This uses a simple procedure but requires effective planning and classroom management. The following content outlines the procedure required to adequately implement the experience into a group setting.

Safety Notes:

Attention should be given to maintaining an area clear of any obstacles that could pose a danger for the participants. Should the group include individuals with special needs, modifications of accommodations will need to be addressed so they are not at a disadvantage experientially.

Getting Started:

Prior to the Activity: Before the participants are gathered in their whole group, make certain that the meeting space will accommodate the free movement of everyone involved. Be aware of any safety issues that could be a problem—split level classrooms, equipment or materials that could be a hazard or obstacle, etc.

Make sets of the small cards; make certain that the number of sets is equal to the total number of cooperative groups to be set up, and that the number of each type is the same as the number of individuals that will fill that group. For example, if there are eight different cooperative groups, you will prepare eight different card sets. If each group will contain three individuals, you will make three small cards of each type (3 flames, 3 rockets, 3 bowling balls, etc). Should you need to have more people in one group than the other, make additional copies of the cards for that set. At the end of the preparation, you should have a total number of small cards that equals the total number of participants in each group. The number of different images used on the cards should equal the total number of cooperative groups involved.

Make one large copy of each different type of image used in the card sets prepared. If you have eight different cooperative groups, you will prepare eight different large pictures. It is helpful to put each picture in a protective sleeve to preserve it during the experience.

Arrange the learning environment so that each cooperative group has a work area or space to report to following the whole group interaction. It is helpful if the area has a flat surface for the groups to work around during the experiences that will follow. Place one of the large pictures at each station.

Materials Needed:
- Sets of small cards
- A large version of each different picture featured on the small cards
- Adequate space for free movement of the whole group
- Work stations or meeting spaces for cooperative groups

Procedure:

Inform the participants that they are going to engage in a whole group experience that will move them into smaller groups. Indicate that each student will receive a card that matches the cards of others in the group. It will be their job to not only find the individuals who match their own card, the group must then find the work station in the room that has a larger version of their similar card. Point out the arrangement of the room, including the area for the whole group movement, as well as the area where the smaller groups will gather. Inform them that as soon as they find their group members and their group home, they are to become acquainted with one another as quickly as possible, and be prepared to begin the phase that follows. Allow time for questions and answers, and point out safety measures that are needed. Provide a time limit if necessary. Pass out the small cards, face down and, when every one has a card, have each of them turn over the cards and begin the procedure.

Card Content Options

You Might Be An Engineer If...
- You take things apart to see how they work . . .
- When you ride in a car, you see new places to add cup holders, MP3 connections and speakers.
- You know vector calculus but you can't remember how to do long division.
- You start disagreeing with movies and TV shows on scientific aspects.
- You always remind people that the ships in Star Wars and Star Trek should be silent in space.
- You laugh at jokes about mathematicians.
- You go on the rides at Disneyland and sit backwards to see how they do the special effects.
- You have a pet named after a scientist.
- Your favorite James Bond character is "Q," the guy who makes the gadgets.
- The salesperson at Best Buy can't answer any of your questions.
- You actually enjoy going to Calculus class.
- You think a mole is a unit of amount, rather than a small furry animal in your lawn.
- You have many half-broken objects in your house that you refuse to throw away with the hope that you can someday fix them.
- When you were a kid, tried to invent various contraptions with the hope of making money.

When you ride in a car, you see new places to add cup holders, MP3 connections and speakers.

When you ride in a car, you see new places to add cup holders, MP3 connections and speakers.

When you ride in a car, you see new places to add cup holders, MP3 connections and speakers.

When you ride in a car, you see new places to add cup holders, MP3 connections and speakers.

When you open a package, you automatically see ways it could've used less cardboard, paper, or plastic.

When you open a package, you automatically see ways it could've used less cardboard, paper, or plastic.

When you open a package, you automatically see ways it could've used less cardboard, paper, or plastic.

When you open a package, you automatically see ways it could've used less cardboard, paper, or plastic.

This page may be photocopied for use in the classroom.

You start disagreeing with movies and TV shows on scientific aspects.

You start disagreeing with movies and TV shows on scientific aspects.

You start disagreeing with movies and TV shows on scientific aspects.

You start disagreeing with movies and TV shows on scientific aspects.

When you were younger, you tried to invent various contraptions with the hope of making money.

When you were younger, you tried to invent various contraptions with the hope of making money.

When you were younger, you tried to invent various contraptions with the hope of making money.

When you were younger, you tried to invent various contraptions with the hope of making money.

You go on the rides at Disneyland and sit backwards to see how they do the special effects.

You go on the rides at Disneyland and sit backwards to see how they do the special effects.

You go on the rides at Disneyland and sit backwards to see how they do the special effects.

You go on the rides at Disneyland and sit backwards to see how they do the special effects.

You always remind people that the ships in Star Wars and Star Trek should be silent in space.

You always remind people that the ships in Star Wars and Star Trek should be silent in space.

You always remind people that the ships in Star Wars and Star Trek should be silent in space.

You always remind people that the ships in Star Wars and Star Trek should be silent in space.

This page may be photcopied for use in the classroom.

You take things apart to see how they work.

You take things apart to see how they work.

You take things apart to see how they work.

You take things apart to see how they work.

You have many half-broken objects in your house that you refuse to throw away with the hope that you can someday fix them.

You have many half-broken objects in your house that you refuse to throw away with the hope that you can someday fix them.

You have many half-broken objects in your house that you refuse to throw away with the hope that you can someday fix them.

You have many half-broken objects in your house that you refuse to throw away with the hope that you can someday fix them.

When you ride in a car, you see new places to add cup holders, MP3 connections and speakers.

When you open a package, you automatically see ways it could've used less cardboard, paper, or plastic.

You start disagreeing with movies and TV shows on scientific aspects.

When you were younger, you tried to invent various contraptions with the hope of making money.

You go on the rides at Disneyland and sit backwards to see how they do the special effects.

You always remind people that the ships in Star Wars and Star Trek should be silent in space.

You take things apart to see how they work.

This page may be photcopied for use in the classroom.

You have many half-broken objects in your house that you refuse to throw away with the hope that you can someday fix them.

The World Stops Without Engineers

Carousel Activity of Engineering Careers

Time Required: 25-40 minutes

How this Learning Experience Meets the National Science Education Standards:

As a result of activities in grades 5-8, all students should develop:

Content Standard A: Science as Inquiry
Abilities Necessary to Do Scientific Inquiry
- Use appropriate tools and techniques to gather, analyze and interpret data
- Think critically and logically to make the relationships between evidence and explanations.
- Recognize and analyze alternative explanations and predictions.

Content Standard G: History and Nature of Science
Science as a Human Endeavor
- Women and men of various social and ethnic backgrounds engage in activities of science, engineering, and related fields; some scientists work in teams, and some work alone, but all communicate extensively with others.
- Science requires different abilities, depending on such factors as the field and study and the type of inquiry.

Overview:

The objective of the following activity is for students to become more aware that engineers have a hand in designing everything.

How to Do a Carousel Activity:

- Divide the class into cooperative groups.
- Assign areas of the room that will serve as "stations" for the activity.
- At each station there should be a task, question, or reading to be completed.
- Explain to the students that they will have a specific amount of time to complete the task that is required at each station. While at the station, they must work as a group and remain there until the signal to rotate is given. They are not to move ahead or try to work ahead during the activity. If they do not finish their task within the time allotted, the groups must still rotate to the next station when told to do so. Encourage them to be focused and work together!
- At the end of the rotation series, each group will have completed the entire assignment given for the carousel activity.
- Walk through the route or path if necessary to insure that the students are aware of the direction they need to rotate.
- Ask the students if they have any questions concerning the procedure or activity.
- Announce how much time they will have at each station.
- Have each of the groups go on to a different station, staggering the groups if possible.
- Begin the activity and monitor the groups as time is kept.
- When the rotations are complete, have a follow up discussion with the groups.

Safety Notes:

Attention should be given to maintaining an area clear of any obstacles that could pose a danger for the participants. Should the group include individuals with special needs, modifications or accommodations will need to be addressed so they are not at a disadvantage experientially.

Getting Started:

1. Copy the 15 carousel sheets and place at 15 different stations around the room.
2. Decide the route or path that the students will rotate through the carousel.

Materials Needed:

- One "Engineering Career Carousel Answer Sheet" and one "Top 20 Engineering Disciplines" sheet per team
- Timer

Procedure:

1. Break students into 15 groups. Groups can be 2, 3 or 4 students each.
2. Assemble one group at each station and give the group a carousel answer sheet.
3. Explain to the students that they will have one minute to work as a group to determine which type of engineer does the job shown on the paper at each station. While at the station, they must and remain there until the signal to rotate is given. They are not to move ahead, or try to work ahead during the activity. If they do not finish their task within the time allotted, their team must still rotate to the next station when told to do so. Encourage them to be focused and work together at each station!
4. When you are satisfied that all of the teams are ready, begin the activity. After 60 seconds, tell the students to move to the next station. Continue until the students have worked at every station.
5. Facilitate a discussion that builds on the students' responses.

1. What Type of Engineer Designs Roller Coasters?

2. What Type of Engineer Designs Running Shoes?

This page may be photcopied for use in the classroom.

3. What Percentage of all Engineering Degrees Went To Women Last Year?

4. What Type of Engineer Designed the Bobsled Course for the Winter Olympics?

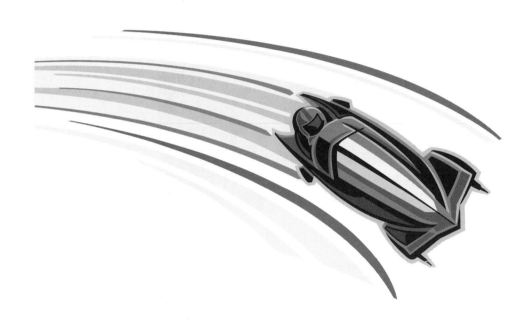

This page may be photcopied for use in the classroom.

5. What Type of Engineer Invented the Ear Thermometer?

6. What Type of Engineer Designs the Microchips that are in your Computer, Stereo and TV?

This page may be photcopied for use in the classroom.

7. What Type of Engineer Designs Golf Balls?

8. What Type of Engineer Ensures That We Have Clean Drinking Water?

This page may be photcopied for use in the classroom.

9. What Type of Engineer Makes Chocolate taste so good? (Hint: they also package our food for maximum freshness.)

10. What Type of Engineer Invented Bubble Gum?
(hint: it was a mistake)

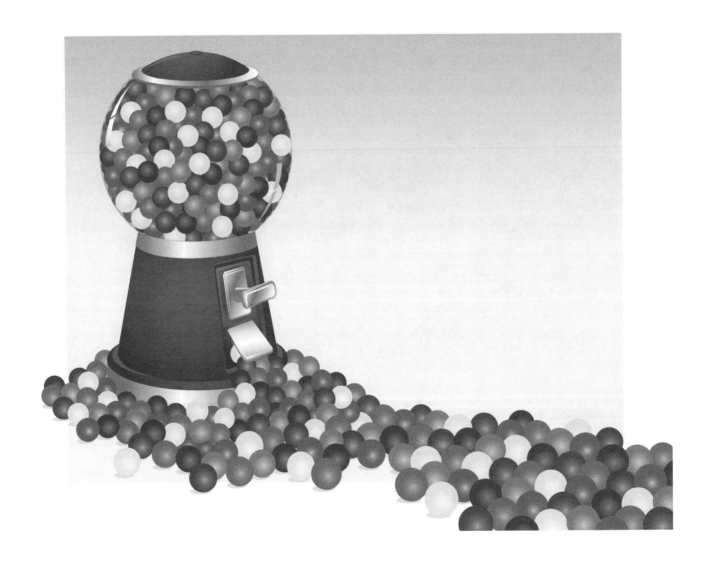

This page may be photcopied for use in the classroom.

11. What Type of Engineer Designs iPods and other MP3 Players So You Can Listen to Your Favorite Music?

Engineers Make a Difference™

12. What Type of Engineer Designs the Robots That Can Go Inside your Body to Find Blood Clots?

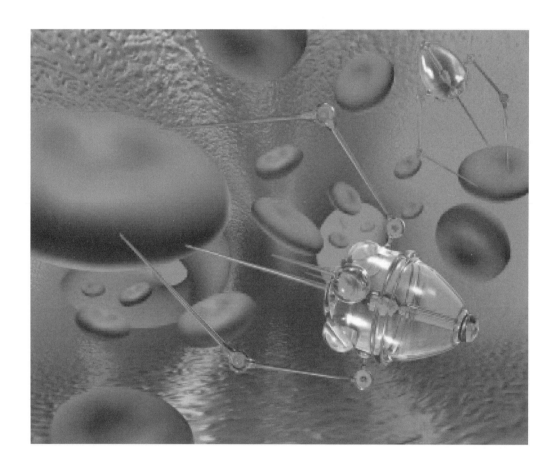

This page may be photcopied for use in the classroom.

13. What Type of Engineer Designs Bicycles?

14. What Type of Engineer Designs Tractors? (Hint: this type of engineer may also work in a lab studying the effects of corn grown indoors.)

This page may be photcopied for use in the classroom.

15. What type of engineer controls the crowd at a theme or amusement park?

Engineering Career Carousel Answer Sheet

1. _____

2. _____

3. _____

4. _____

5. _____

6. _____

7. _____

8. _____

9. _____

10. _____

11. _____

12. _____

13. _____

14. _____

15. _____

Engineering Career Carousel Answers

. What type of engineer designs roller coasters?
   Answer: **Mechanical, civil and structural engineering are the most common majors.**

2. What type of engineer designs running shoes?
   Answer: **Biomedical and chemical engineers**

3. What percentage of all engineering degrees went to women last year?
   Answer: **In 2012, it was 18%. Check your facts if last year was different than 2012.**

4. What type of engineer designed the bobsled course for the Winter Olympics?
   Answer: **Civil Engineer - Four-man bobsleds can reach speeds of 80-90 mph, with up to four G-forces in the curves, depending on the track.**

5. What type of engineer invented the ear thermometer?
   Answer: **Biomedical Engineer**

6. What type of engineer designs the microchips that are in your computer, stereo, TV, etc?
   Answer: **Ceramic (division of materials engineering) and Electrical Engineers**

7. What type of engineer designs golf balls?
   Answer: **Aeronautical and Aerospace Engineers**

8. What type of engineer ensures that we have clean drinking water?
   Answer: **Environmental Engineers**

9. What type of engineer makes chocolate taste so good? (Hint: They also package our food for maximum freshness
   Answer: **Food Engineers (division of chemical engineering)**

10. What type of engineer invented bubble gum? (hint: it was a mistake)
    Answer: **Chemical Engineer**

11. What type of engineer designs iPods and other MP3 players so you can listen to your favorite music?
    Answer: **Electrical, Software and Computer Engineers**

12. What type of engineer designs the robots that can go inside your body to find blood clots?
    Answer: **Electrical, Mechanical, and Biomedical are the most common.**

13. What type of engineer designs bicycles?
    Answer: **Mechanical Engineers**

14. What type of engineer designs tractors? (Hint: this type of engineer may also work in a lab studying the effects of corn grown indoors.)
    Answer: **Agricultural Engineers**

15. What type of engineer controls the crowd at a theme or amusement park?
    Answer: **Industrial Engineers**

Top 20 Engineering Disciplines

Engineering is a diverse and challenging field of study. With more than 25 major branches of engineering and 100 specialties, there is something for everyone who pursues the field.

1. **Aeronautical / Aerospace Engineering** - Aeronautical/aerospace engineers design and develop technology for commercial aviation, national defense and space exploration. They may help design and manufacture military aircraft, missiles, helicopters, and spacecraft. Within this field, they may specialize in the structure of the aircraft, aerodynamics, guidance and control, propulsion and design, manufacturing, or a certain type of aircraft. Commercial airliners, military aircraft, space shuttles, satellites, rockets, and helicopters are all within reach for talented aeronautical engineers, who may also be referred to as astronautical, aviation or rocket engineers.

2. **Agricultural and Biological Engineering** - Biological and agricultural engineering, two closely integrated disciplines often called biological systems (biosystems), bioresources, or natural resources engineering, are concerned with finding solutions for life on a small planet. Our swelling world population places great demands on our limited natural resources, and biological and agricultural engineers work to ensure that we have the necessities of life: safe and plentiful food to eat, pure water to drink, clean fuel and energy sources, and a safe, healthy environment.

3. **Architectural Engineering** - Architectural engineers apply engineering principles to the design and technical systems of buildings - mainly their structural, mechanical, plumbing and lighting/electrical design. Engineers need to be aesthetic as well as technical, creative as well as practical. They need to know if what looks good on paper is also technically possible.

4. **Biomedical Engineering** - The objective of biomedical engineering is to enhance health care by solving complex medical problems using engineering principles. Those who specialize in this field want to serve the public, work with health care professionals, and interact with living systems. This broad field allows a large choice of sub-specialties. Many students say they choose biomedical engineering because it is people-oriented. The field includes many branches: biomechanical, bioelectrical, biochemical, rehabilitation, clinical, and genetic engineering. There are also many sub-specialties within biomedical engineering such as surgical lasers, telemedicine, nuclear medicine, and clinical computer systems.

5. **Chemical Engineering** - Everything that our senses enjoy consists of chemicals in one way or another. Chemical engineers have worked on creating the purple rose that has no thorns, the caramel on a caramel apple, and even your tennis shoes. The chemical engineering profession has improved water and waste systems, created new drugs and drug delivery systems, and improved the crop yields for farmers. Most chemical engineers work in manufacturing, pharmaceuticals, healthcare, design and construction, pulp and paper, petrochemicals, food processing, specialty chemicals, microelectronics, electronic and advanced materials, polymers, business services, biotechnology, and the environmental health and safety industries.

6. **Civil Engineering** - Traditionally, civil engineers planned and designed such things as roads, bridges, high-rises, dams, and airports. Because of population growth and a booming economy, however, the civil engineer now also designs new things such as underwater tunnels, new and better wastewater treatment plants, solutions for highway congestion, and special tracks for the magnetic levitation trains of the future.

7. **Computer Engineering** - Computer engineering deals with the many aspects of computer systems. These engineers may design computer systems, networks, operating systems, or software. They may design the future automobile dashboard computers that will monitor engine functions. Engineers in this field design computer chips, circuits, equipment, and systems; plan computer layouts; and formulate mathematical models to solve technical problems on computer. They design, develop, and test computer hardware and peripheral equipment. They also design, develop, and maintain software programs and software systems.

8. **Electrical Engineering** - The developments of electrical and electronic engineers are everywhere. There are thousands of electrical devices and systems available today that electrical engineers have somehow touched. Anything you plug into the wall – stereos, computers, microwaves, televisions, power tools, air-conditioners, and major appliances – has been touched by an electrical engineer. Even things you can't plug into the wall – satellites, cellular phones, and beepers – have been designed, manufactured, or modified by electrical engineers.

9. **Environmental Engineering** - Environmental engineering focuses on the development of a sustainable future, preventing pollution, assessing the environmental impact of everything, water distribution systems, recycling methods, sewage treatment plants, and pesticide prevention. This fast-growing field offers a challenging and satisfying chance to protect the health and safety of people and our environment. These earth-friendly professionals concern themselves with preventing and fixing problems caused by industrialization. They concentrate on delivering better environmental conditions for the public through knowledge, research, a caring attitude, and common sense.

10. **Heating, Ventilating, Refrigerating, and Air-Conditioning Engineering** - Heating, ventilating, refrigeration, and air-conditioning (HVR&AC) engineers have dramatically improved our lives. HVR&AC engineers develop systems to

68

create and maintain safe and comfortable environments. Airplanes, trains, schools, cars, and computer rooms are only a handful of the environments that depend on HVR&AC engineers.

1. **Industrial Engineering -** Industrial engineers figure out how to improve everything. They work with people to help them do things better. Industrial engineers save employers money by streamlining systems, often making the workplace better for employees too. They improve productivity and quality while saving time and money. Industrial engineers work on all type of businesses. They see the big picture and focus on what makes a system perform efficiently, safely, and effectively to produce the highest quality.

2. **Manufacturing Engineering -** Just as the mechanical engineer designs parts, the manufacturing engineer designs the processes that make them. Wherever there's a production process to be designed and managed, you'll find manufacturing engineers at work. They work with plant managers, production supervisors, CNC programmers, quality managers, product designers, and R&D staff on issues ranging from evaluating new technology and choosing equipment and suppliers to leading industry-wide standards development to reorganizing a plant into a more efficient production system.

3. **Materials Engineering -** Materials engineers design, fabricate, and test materials. They may work to make automobiles lighter and more fuel efficient by creating stronger and lighter metals. They may help to create artificial knees and elbows using special polymers, or they may design new materials for the space ship. A materials engineer can work with any type of material – plastic, wood, ceramic, petroleum or metals –and create completely new synthetic products by rearranging molecular structure.

4. **Mechanical Engineering -** Mechanical engineers is one of the broadest and most diverse disciplines. Mechanical engineers design, develop, and manufacture every kind of vehicle, power system, machine, and tool: jet engines, steam engines, power plants, underwater structures, tractors for food production, hydraulic systems, transportation systems, medical devices, sports equipment, smart materials, materials and structures for space travel, measurement devices, and more. Any type of machine that produces, transmits, or uses power is most likely the product of a mechanical engineer.

5. **Metallurgical Engineering -** Metallurgical engineers turn raw materials into useful products. Metallurgical engineering includes processing mineral and chemical resources into metallic, ceramic or polymeric materials; creating new high strength or high performance materials; or developing new ways to refine and process materials for new consumer applications.

6. **Nuclear Engineering -** Nuclear engineering falls into three major areas of benefit to mankind: nuclear medicine, agricultural uses and pest control, and nuclear energy. Nuclear engineers search for efficient and beneficial ways to use the power generated from splitting an atom, and they research peaceful ways to use nuclear energy and radiation.

7. **Naval Architecture, Marine Engineering, and Ocean Engineering -** Naval architecture, marine engineering, and ocean engineering are professions that integrate disciplines such as materials science and mechanical, civil, and electrical engineering. These engineers and architects design, build, operate, and maintain ships such as aircraft carriers, submarines, tankers, tugboats, sailboats, and yachts. They also develop underwater structures, underwater robots, and oil rigs. They develop transportation systems, plan new uses for waterways, design deep-water ports, and integrate the land and water transportation systems and methods. They are concerned with discovering, producing, and transporting offshore petroleum as sources of energy and developing new ways to protect marine wildlife and beaches against the unwanted consequences of offshore oil production.

8. **Software Engineering -** Software engineering is on the cutting edge of technology. Software enables us to use computers. It is the translator between humans and computers. Without software, a computer would be nothing but ones and zeros. The current demand for software engineers far exceeds the supply. The largest employers of software engineers include familiar names such as Microsoft, Motorola, Autodesk, Netscape, Adobe, Symantec, Nintendo, and Corel. However, there are thousands of software manufacturers that hire software engineers.

9. **Structural Engineering -** Structural engineering focuses not only on the design and development of structures, such as houses, coliseums, bridges, and shopping malls, but on the design and development of materials that will create these structures. The structural engineering profession offers exciting challenges and potential for growth. Each day brings new and more sophisticated materials that will change the shape and the future of structures. Structural engineers must be creative and resourceful. They must visualize the framework of a structure and determine what forces will produce what loads upon it. Many structural engineers in California design buildings that are able to sustain ground-shaking (earthquake) loads.

10. **Transportation Engineering -** Transportation engineering is a branch of civil engineering that aims to allow people and goods to move safely, rapidly, conveniently, and efficiently. Transportation engineers design streets, highways, and public transportation systems. They design parking lots and traffic flow patterns that will prevent major congestion at busy intersections, shopping malls, and sporting events. They are involved in planning and designing airports, railroads, and busy pedestrian thoroughfares.

Engineering Principles

Measure It!

How this Learning Experience Meets the National Science Education Standards:

NSTA 5-8
Students develop abilities necessary to do scientific inquiry
- Students identify questions that can be measured through scientific inquiry
- Students use appropriate tools and techniques to gather, analyze and interpret data.
- Students think critically and logically to make the relationships between evidence and explanations
- Students communicate scientific procedures and explanations
- Students use mathematics in all aspects of scientific inquiry.

NSTA 9-12
Students develop abilities necessary to do scientific inquiry
- Students identify questions and concepts that guide scientific investigations.
- Students identify questions and conduct scientific investigations.
- Students use technology and mathematics to improve investigations and communications.
- Students formulate and revise scientific explanations and models using logic and evidence.

NCTM 6-8
Students understand numbers, ways of representing numbers, relationships among numbers, and number systems.

Students understand the meaning of operations and how they relate to one another.
- Students understand the meaning and effects of arithmetic operations with fractions, decimals and integers.

Students compute fluently and make reasonable estimates.

Students analyze characteristics and properties of two and three dimensional shapes and develop mathematical arguments about geometric relationships.
- Students understand relationships among the angles, side lengths, perimeters, areas, and volumes of similar objects.

Students use visualization, spatial reasoning and geometric modeling to solve problems.
- Students understand, select, and use units of appropriate size and type to measure angles, perimeter, area, surface area and volume.

Students apply appropriate techniques, tools and formulas to determine measurements.

NCTM 9-12
Students compute fluently and make reasonable estimates.
- Students judge the reasonableness of numerical computations and their results.
- Students draw reasonable conclusions about a situation being modeled.

Students understand measurement attributes of objects and the units, systems, and processes of measurement.
- Students make decisions about units and scales that are appropriate for problem situations involving measurement.

ITEEA 6-9
Students develop an understanding of engineering design.

- Students learn to design and use instruments to gather data.

Objective

In this activity, students will compare independent systems designed to measure the same object.

Background

It's important to note that precision in measurement is relative. For example, if you have a handful of strawberries and want to find out which is biggest, you can use any scale to measure the mass because you are comparing them relative to each other. You just have to be sure that you use the same scale to measure each berry.

If you are interested in doing a medical experiment and need an exact dosage (mass) to administer to a patient, you want to use the most precise scale possible. A precise scale will give the same reading as a scale in any other part of the world at different times. The measurement is not relative to other doses of medicine, it's an absolute value.

Getting Started

1. Collect the materials needed for the activity.
2. Determine the size of the groups engaging in the experiment.
3. Identify a work area that can accommodate the measurements needed for each part of the activity.
4. Copy the student sheets.

Materials Needed Per Group of Students

- Masking Tape
- Balance Beam
- Digital Scale
- Stopwatch
- Wrist watch with second hand or timer
- Rolatape
- Tape Measure
- Yardstick
- Penny
- Student Sheets

Procedure

Part 1

1. Assemble students in teams.
2. Have students locate the balance beam and a digital scale. *The best digital scale to use is one that measures grams. However, if your digital scale does not measure grams, you may want the students to convert their data to the same scale (or you can have a reference chart to help). Just note that this is another source of possible error.*
3. Have students write their hypothesis for the balance beam vs. the digital scale on Part I of their student sheet.

4. Have students choose three small objects to measure the weight. *Any objects will do so long as the students use the same objects for each series of measurements.*
5. Instruct students to weigh the first object on the balance beam and record their findings on their student sheet.
6. Instruct students to weigh the first object on the digital scale and record their findings on their student sheet.
7. Instruct students to follow the same procedure with the other two objects.
8. Have students complete the remainder of Part I of their student sheet.

Part 2

1. Have students locate the rolatape and a tape measure.
2. Have students write their hypothesis for the rolatape vs. the tape measure on Part II of their student sheet.
3. Have students mark (masking tape works good) two locations approximately 10-15 feet apart.
4. Using the rolatape, measure the length between the two marks and record the measurement on their student sheet.
5. Using the tape measure, measure the length between the two marks and record the measurement on their student sheet.
6. Have students complete the rolatape vs. the tape measure section of their student sheet.

Part 3

1. Have students locate their stopwatch.
2. Make sure one person in each group has a watch with either a second hand or with a digital seconds reading.
3. Have students locate a yardstick.
4. Using an object such as a penny, have one member of each team hold the penny in the air at the same height as the yard stick.
5. Using the stopwatch, have students time the time that it takes the penny to hit the floor or table-top.
6. Have students record this time on their data sheet.
7. Have students repeat the procedure three times and record the data.
8. Using a watch, have students time the seconds that it takes the penny to hit the floor or table-top.
9. Have students record this time on their data sheet.
10. Have students repeat the procedure three times and record the data.
11. Have students complete the remainder of Part III of their student sheet.

Measure It Student Sheet
Part I

Balance Beam vs. Digital Scale

Choose three small objects to measure the weight (examples: pencil, a CD and a ruler).

Hypothesis
How do you think the weight of the Balance Beam will compare to the Digital Scale?

Data
Weight of the first object on a balance beam _____

Weight of the first object on a Digital Scale _____

Weight of the 2nd object on a balance beam _____

Weight of the 2nd object on a Digital Scale _____

Weight of the 3rd object on a balance beam _____

Weight of the 3rd object on a Digital Scale _____

Comparison
How does your data compare to your original hypothesis?

When is it better to use a Digital Scale?

When is it better to use a Balance Beam?

This page may be photocopied for use in the classroom.

Measure It Student Sheet
Part II

Rolatape vs. Tape Measure

Hypothesis
How do you think the distance measured by the Rolatape will compare to the distance measured by the Tape Measure?

Mark (masking tape works good) two locations approximately 10-15 feet apart in a straight line.

Distance between the two marks measured by the Rolatape _____

Distance between the two marks measured by the Tape Measure _____

Comparison
How does your data compare to your original hypothesis?

When is it better to use a Rolatape?

When is it better to use a Tape Measure?

Measure It Student Sheet
Part III

Stopwatch vs. Wrist Watch

Hypothesis
How do you think the time measured by the Stopwatch will compare to the time measured by the Wrist Watch?

1. Using an object such as a penny, have one member on your team hold the penny in the air at the same height as the end of a yard stick.
2. Using the stopwatch, record the time that it takes the penny to hit the floor or table-top.
3. Repeat the procedure three times and record the data.
4. Using your watch, record the time that it takes the penny to hit the floor or table-top.
5. Repeat the procedure three times and record the data.

Data

	Trial #1	Trial #2	Trial #3
Time measured by the Stopwatch			
Time measured by the Wrist Watch			

What is the average time measured by the Stopwatch? _____

What is the average time measured by the Wrist Watch? _____

Comparison
How does your data compare to your original hypothesis?

When is it better to use a Stopwatch?

When is it better to use a Wrist Watch?

Name at least 3 possible sources of error when measuring time in the above example?

This page may be photocopied for use in the classroom.

Born to Rock!
Engineering a Balancing Act That Rocks

Time required 30-45 minutes

How this Learning Experience Meets the National Science Education Standards:

NSTA 5-8

Students develop abilities necessary to do scientific inquiry
- Students identify questions that can be measured through scientific inquiry.
- Students use appropriate tools and techniques to gather, analyze and interpret data.
- Students think critically and logically to make the relationships between evidence and explanations.
- Students recognize and analyze alternative explanations and predictions.
- Students communicate scientific procedures and explanations.
- Students use mathematics in all aspects of scientific inquiry.

Students develop abilities for technological design
- Students evaluate completed technological designs or products.

NCTM 6-8
- Students select and use appropriate statistical methods to analyze data.
- Students develop and evaluate inferences and predictions that are based on data.
- Students recognize and apply mathematics in contexts outside of mathematics.

ITEEA 6-9

Students develop an understanding of engineering design.
- Students learn that modeling, testing, evaluating, and modifying are used to transform ideas into practical solutions.

Students develop abilities to apply the design process.
- Students learn to apply a design process to solve problems in and beyond the laboratory-classroom.
- Students learn to make a product or system and document the solution.

Students develop abilities to assess the impact of products and systems.
- Students learn to design and use instruments to gather data.

NCTE K-12
- Students adjust their use of spoken, written and visual language to communicate effectively with a variety of audiences and for different purposes.

Objective

To verify Newton's First Law of Motion and balance an object (find it's equilibrium).

Teacher Information:

In order to effectively monitor and guide students during their development process, teachers should familiarize themselves with the following procedure for creating the balancing act:

1. Create a balancing person from three craft sticks.
2. Cut two craft sticks in half, then shorten the third by approximately one inch.
3. Use these four pieces of craft stick to create a stick person, attaching the arms and legs with a glue stick. Arms and legs should be extending down at a similar angle.
4. Use the sandpaper to create feet surface that can stand on the yogurt container or block of wood. It is helpful to sand the feet at an angle to make them more pointed in shape.
5. Create a balancing stick from the remaining craft sticks. It is essential that the balancing stick extend below the stick person's feet.
6. Add a ball of modeling clay to each end of the balancing stick. It will require trial and error to determine the correct amount of modeling clay needed. Too much and your person won't rock for long, too little and they won't stand up properly.
7. Design a head by drawing on the Styrofoam ball then insert it onto the rounded edge of the craft stick body.
8. Stand the person on the on the upside-down yogurt container or wooden block then gently push it so that it will rock with the objective being for it to rock as long as possible.
9. See the sample product in the picture below.

This is also a good time to introduce engineering careers that connect to music, such as music engineering.

Commonly referred to as sound engineers or audio engineers, music engineers work to make sure all aspects regarding sound and music production function accordingly. Music engineers not only work in music recording but also work with the design of sound systems and musical venues such as concert halls and stadiums where their primary responsibilities include managing electrical equipment during music recording sessions and overseeing the design of sound equipment for sites in which musical events will be held.

They are also concerned with the acoustics of production and give attention to the details of reproducing music, sound mixing and producing various sound effects. Music engineers work closely with music producers and directors as well as architects when working on sound design and acoustics for the building of new musical venues.

Training of musical engineers varies depending on which aspect of the field an individual pursues. According to Oracle ThinkQuest Education Foundation, a degree in engineering is required for those who wish to work on the design of sound systems, musical venues and the design of musical instruments. Music engineers working in recording studios and music production have opportunities to complete vocational training programs, attend community colleges or obtain a bachelor's degree in music production. Regardless of the level of education obtained, hands-on experience such as an internship will provide the most training. For individuals interested in a career in music engineering, keeping up with the latest technologies in computer electronics and digital sound production is helpful. Music engineers also benefit from possessing background knowledge in music and even the ability to play a musical instrument. An interest in physics as it relates to sound is also a plus.

Safety Notes:

Students will need to cut their craft sticks with scissors so emphasize safety as they work with them. If needed, have them bring their craft sticks to you with instructions on where to cut and you cut each for them. With older students you may want to utilize a hot glue gun rather than glue sticks.

Materials per Team

- Six (6) small craft sticks
- Styrofoam ball (about the size of a golf ball)
- Modeling clay
- Glue stick
- Scissors
- Markers
- Metric rulers
- Empty, clean yogurt container or small block of wood
- Paper
- Sandpaper
- Stopwatch

Getting Started

1. Gather materials for each collaborative group.
2. If appropriate, have the craft sticks already cut for the students groups.
3. Determine how much time will be allotted for completing the design challenge.
4. Be sure each group has adequate space and a flat surface for developing and testing its prototype.
5. Prepare the Entry Document from the Rock and Roll Hall of Fame and if possible, arrange for a guest to come and deliver the document to add authenticity to the learning experience.
6. Determine if the students will be allowed to listen to their music and do additional research on their chosen artist as an extension of the challenge.
7. Plan for assessment criteria that will be utilized as the prototypes are tested.
8. Consider allowing student-created extensions to the learning experience. Examples could be a creative writing exercise, development of additional characters to build a community of unique balancing acts based on other entertainment or sports personalities.

Procedure:

1. Assemble students into collaborative groups.
2. Present students with the entry document that defines the design challenge.
3. Have the students identify which music and/or artist they will focus on as they work through the challenge.
4. Discuss any guidelines groups may need to work within.
5. Emphasize that the objective is for the final product to rock as long as possible.
6. Encourage students to sketch plans, create prototypes from the paper, and test their products as they proceed with the design process.
7. Provide each group with the materials available for the design of the final prototype product.
8. Announce time frame allowed.
9. Monitor students as they work.
10. At the end of the time frame, facilitate testing of prototypes with each group observing and making notes.
11. Debrief students afterward about the design process as well as the testing and challenges involved.
12. If time permits, allow each group to revisit its design and enhance or improve it based on knowledge gained from the experience.

Dear Engineering Students:

The Rock and Roll Hall of Fame + Museum is working to develop a series of activities that will connect the classroom experiences of young people across America to the ongoing development of our museum. As part of our growth, we are interested in putting together a series of activities that will engage students in science and engineering while connecting to their favorite music and artists. You have been selected to help us in this mission and it is our hope that you will accept the challenge and successfully produce a prototype for our "Born to Rock" series. Your teacher has additional details and instructions so we encourage you to listen carefully and then get ready to rock out. We look forward to seeing who in this class will end up being the best rocker and thus help us spread the rock and roll spirit. Rock on!

The Rock and Roll Hall of Fame + Museum Board
Born to Rock Challenge
Student Sheet #2

Using the materials provided, complete the following challenge so that your rocker rocks longer than any other in the class:

- Create a stick person out of three craft sticks— sticks can be cut and attached as needed

- Using the sandpaper, modify the "feet" of the stick person so they can stand and rock at the same time

- Create a balancing stick out of three craft sticks—the stick must be able to attach to the stick person

- Add a ball of modeling clay to each end of the balancing stick so that the stick person can both stand up and rock

- Create a rock and roll head for your stick person using the Styrofoam ball provided

- Stand your rocker on its stage and gently push so that it rocks

- Time how long your rocker will rock

- If needed, modify your design to enhance its ability to rock

- Prepare for the class test

The rocker that rocks the longest wins the challenge

Forces - Compression and Tension

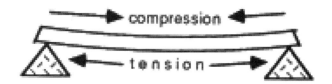

Understanding the Effects of Pushing and Pulling

How this Learning Experience Meets the National Science Education Standards:

NSTA 5-8
Students develop abilities necessary to do scientific inquiry
- Students identify questions that can be measured through scientific inquiry
- Students use appropriate tools and techniques to gather, analyze and interpret data.
- Students think critically and logically to make the relationships between evidence and explanations

NCTM 6-8
Students develop and evaluate inferences and predictions that are based on data.

ITEEA 6-9
- Students learn to design and use instruments to gather data.
- Students learn to make a product or system and document the solution.
- Students develop abilities to assess the impact of products and systems.

Objective

Learn the difference between compression and tension and identify which members in a structure are in tension and which are in compression.

Background

The words load, compression and tension are words commonly used in the design of a bridge. When a load is placed in the middle of a beam, it tries to compress on the top of the bridge thus creating what is called compression. The bottom of the bridge tries to pull apart thus creating what is referred to by engineers as tension.

Racking is a kind of stress that distorts a square or rectangle causing it to become a parallelogram.

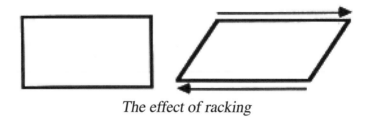

The effect of racking

To strengthen a square or rectangle, a diagonal brace (aka truss) converts the rectangle into two triangles, thus making the figure much stronger. Converting figures into triangles is one which engineers use extensively in bridge designs since triangles are the strongest possible figure.

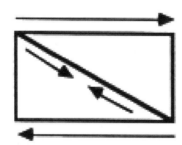

Use of a diagonal brace to strengthen a rectangle

Safety

Knives and blades are very sharp and should be used with care. Don't cut too closely to the fingers. Using a Timber Cutter can help ensure that no fingers get cut. If students are using a hobby knife, make sure the cutting edge of the blade is always facing away from the person that is doing the cutting. Students should be closely monitored. Inexperienced students may prefer to have the instructor do some of the cutting, particularly on smaller items.

Be careful of T-pins - their sharp points can be painful!

Materials

- 1/8"x1/8" Balsa wood strips
- Timber cutter or hobby knife
- T-pins
- Ruler
- Colored Markers (Red, Blue, Green and Yellow)
- Student sheet

Student Procedure

1. Cut seven pieces of balsa wood to 5 centimeters long and one piece to 7.1 centimeters long.

2. Assemble 4 of the 5 cm pieces into a square and 3 of the 5 cm pieces into a triangle. Using T-pins and miter joints, join the corners of each shape. You may have to sand the ends to get them to fit together at a 45 degree angle.

3. Write a hypothesis on your student sheet stating how you think the strength of the two shapes will compare.

4. Use four different colored markers and color each side of the square differently. Use red for the top, blue for the bottom, green on the right and yellow on the left.

5. Stand the square upright and using your finger, apply a load (push in a downward direction) at A (middle of the red side). Be careful not to apply so much load that the square breaks. What happens to the frame? Record your observations on the student sheet.

6. Consider each of the four members of the square frame. Is each member under compression or tension as the load is applied at Point A? Record your answers in Table A on your student sheet.

7. With the frame in an upright position, apply a load at B in the direction shown (junction of red and green). Again, be careful not to apply so much force that the square breaks. What happens to the frame? Record your observations on your student sheet.

8. Consider each of the four members of the square frame. Is each member under compression or tension as the load is applied at Point B? Record your answers in Table A on your student sheet.

9. Using the 7.1 cm piece, add a truss or a rigid diagonal to the center of the square with two more T-pins.

10. Place the frame in an upright position and apply a load (push with your finger) at C in the direction shown (junction of red and yellow). Be careful not to apply too much load. What happens to the frame? Record your observations on your student sheet.

11. Consider each of the five members of the square frame. Is each member under compression or tension as the load is applied at Point C? Record your answers in Table B on your student sheet.

12. With the frame in an upright position, apply a load (push with your finger) at D in the direction shown (junction of red and yellow). Be careful not to apply too much load. What happens to the frame? Record your observations on your student sheet.

13. Consider each of the five members of the square frame. Is each member under compression or tension as the load is applied at Point D? Record your answers in Table B on your student sheet.

14. What shape do you see when the diagonals are added? Record your answer on your student sheet.

15. Consider the two squares: one without a diagonal and one with a diagonal. Which square resists more force and why? Record your answer on your student sheet.

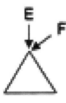

16. Place your triangle in an upright position.

17. Using your finger, apply a load at E in the direction shown. What happens to the frame? Record your answer.

18. Consider each of the three members of the triangle frame. Is each member under compression or tension as the load is applied at Point E? Record your answers in Table C on your student sheet.

19. Apply a load at F in the direction shown. What happens to the frame? Record your answer.

20. Consider each of the three members of the triangle frame. Is each member under compression or tension as the load is applied at Point F? Record your answers in Table B.

21. In table D, rank the strength of the frames and applied loads from 1 to 6 with 1 being the strongest frame and 6 being the weakest frame.

22. Consider the results of your tests based on your recorded data. Does your data support your original hypothesis? Record your answers.

Tension and Compression Student Sheet

1. Hypothesis - How will the strength of the two shapes, the square and the triangle compare?

2. Observation - What happens to the square frame when a load is applied at Point A?

3. Observation - What happens to the square frame when a load is applied at Point B?

4. TABLE A

Point of Force	Member in Question	Compression or Tension?
A	Red	
A	Green	
A	Yellow	
A	Blue	
B	Red	
B	Green	
B	Yellow	
B	Blue	

5. Observation - What happens to the square frame (with a diagonal) when a load is applied at Point C?

6. TABLE B

Point of Force	Member in Question	Compression or Tension?
C	Red	
C	Green	
C	Yellow	
C	Blue	
C	Diagonal	
D	Red	
D	Green	
D	Yellow	
D	Blue	
D	Diagonal	

This page may be photocopied for use in the classroom.

7. Observation - What happens to the square frame (with a diagonal) when a load is applied at Point D?

8. What shape(s) do you see when the diagonal is added to the square?

9. Which square (with or without a diagonal) resists more force and why?

10. Observation - What happens to the triangle frame with Load E is applied?

11. TABLE C		
Point of Force	Member in Question	Compression or Tension?
E	Right	
E	Left	
E	Bottom	
F	Right	
F	Left	
F	Bottom	

12. Observation - What happens to the triangle frame when Load F is applied?

13. TABLE D		
Shape	Point of Force	Frame Strength Ranking
	A	
	B	
	C	
	D	
	E	
	F	

Conclusion

Does your data support your original hypothesis? Why or why not?

Tension and Compression Data Sheet
Teachers Guide - Answer Sheet

TABLE A

Point of Force	Member in Question	Compression or Tension?
A	Red	Compression on the top of the beam Tension on the bottom
A	Green	Compression
A	Yellow	Compression
A	Blue	Tension
B	Red	Compression
B	Green	Compression
B	Yellow	Tension
B	Blue	Tension

TABLE B

Point of Force	Member in Question	Compression or Tension?
C	Red	Compression
C	Green	Tension
C	Yellow	Compression
C	Blue	Tension
C	Diagonal	Tension
D	Red	Compression
D	Green	Compression
D	Yellow	Tension
D	Blue	Tension
D	Diagonal	Compression

TABLE C

Point of Force	Member in Question	Compression or Tension?
E	Right	Compression
E	Left	Compression
E	Bottom	Tension
F	Right	Tension
F	Left	Compression
F	Bottom	Tension

TABLE D		
Shape	Point of Force	Frame Strength Ranking
	A	5
	B	6
	C	4
	D	3
	E	1
	F	2

Tsunami Shelter Platform

Exploring Column Strength, Loads and Forces While Creating a Vertical Evacuation Shelter

How this Learning Experience Meets the National Science Education Standards:

NSTA 5-8
Students develop abilities necessary to do scientific inquiry
- Students identify questions that can be measured through scientific inquiry.
- Students use appropriate tools and techniques to gather, analyze and interpret data.
- Students think critically and logically to make the relationships between evidence and explanations.
- Students recognize and analyze alternative explanations and predictions.
- Students communicate scientific procedures and explanations.
- Students use mathematics in all aspects of scientific inquiry.

Students develop abilities for technological design
- Students evaluate completed technological designs or products.

NCTM 6-8
- Students select and use appropriate statistical methods to analyze data.
- Students develop and evaluate inferences and predictions that are based on data.
- Students recognize and apply mathematics in contexts outside of mathematics.

ITEEA 6-9
Students develop an understanding of engineering design.
- Students learn that modeling, testing, evaluating, and modifying are used to transform ideas into practical solutions.

Students develop abilities to apply the design process.
- Students learn to apply a design process to solve problems in and beyond the laboratory-classroom.
- Students learn to make a product or system and document the solution.

Students develop abilities to assess the impact of products and systems.
- Students learn to design and use instruments to gather data.

NCTE K-12
- Students adjust their use of spoken, written and visual language to communicate effectively with a variety of audiences and for different purposes.

Objective

The purpose of this activity is for students to develop a model solution to a real-world, interdisciplinary problem. The activity ties in natural disasters and engineers as problem solvers.

Background

How does an engineer assist during a natural disaster?
- Engineers work in a team, using the design process to solve many different types of problems.
- Place students into a design team (up to 4 per group) in order to generate some ideas, which they will present to the class.
- Using a collective data gathering strategy, ask students to come up with a list of different ways that engineers can assist during a natural disaster.

Share this data with the class.

Suggestions:
- Have students brainstorm their ideas on a sheet of large construction paper, or butcher paper. As the ideas are collected, have individuals from the group record their responses on a large sheet of paper on the wall or board.
- Group similar ideas together, and create a more general list of how an engineer assists during a natural disaster.
- Display all of this brainstorming, and the final list, for all to see. It is interesting to compare the ideas across classes or grades.

Teacher Notes:

You may want to introduce a video that focuses on tsunami information. There is quite a variety of videos available. Use what you have in your school library. It may be that you have a general natural disaster video, and can pull out the portion that focuses on tsunamis. The purpose of the video, is to let the students see actual footage of a tsunami, and the destructive action that results in the aftermath of the wave.

If a video is not available, you may find some video footage available on the Internet. It's important to remember, however, that regardless on what media you use to share this information, make sure that the video footage is acceptable for the age group in your classroom. Some of the raw video available on natural disasters such as the tsunamis can be quite graphic, so make sure you preview the video prior to showing it to the entire class.

Civil and structural engineers develop structures that can support heavy loads.

In addition, the following concepts can be developed fully through this exploration in engineering design:
- Forces
- Torque
- Center of mass
- Stability
- Tension
- Compression

- Beam strength
- Column strength

Safety Notes:

Participants should be reminded of the safe handling of scissors and pins; in addition, the work area should be clear of obstacles. Movement throughout the work area should be careful.

Getting Started:

1. Collect the materials needed for the challenge.
2. Determine the size of the groups engaging in the experience.
3. Identify a work area that can accommodate the construction and testing of the shelters.
4. Copy student challenge sheets.

Materials Needed Per Group of Students:

- 50 plastic straws
- One (1) meter of masking tape
- 25 paper clips
- 25 index cards
- 15 pieces of paper
- Meter stick
- Student challenge sheets

Procedure:

1. Assemble students into cooperative groups.
2. Challenge each group to construct a vertical evacuation shelter from straws, paper clips, index cards, paper, and 1 meter of tape within the following guidelines:

   - Each group has 30 minutes to complete construction and testing of their shelter
   - The platform must be free-standing and not anchored to the table in any way or leaning against any other structure
   - Each shelter's strength and stability will be tested by placing a weighted object representative of a group of people in the center of the platform
   - The platform must be able to stand freely with the people on it for 30 seconds
   - Groups will get no more materials during the challenge
   - To determine a winner of the challenge, additional weight will be added to the platform with the platform supporting the most weight winning the challenge.

The platform that supports the most weight wins the challenge

Tsunami Shelter
Vertical Evacuation Challenge

Challenge Guidelines:

Construct a tsunami vertical evacuation shelter using only 50 plastic straws, 25 paper clips, 25 index cards, 15 pieces of paper, and one meter of masking tape.

- Each group has 30 minutes to complete construction and testing of their shelter

- The platform must be free-standing and not anchored to the table in any way or leaning against any other structure

- Each platform's strength and stability will be tested by placing a weighted object representative of a group of people in the center of the platform

- The platform must be able to stand freely with the people on it for 30 seconds

- Groups will get no more materials during the challenge

- To determine a winner of the challenge, additional weight will be added to the platform with the platform supporting the most weight winning the challenge.

The platform that supports the most weight wins the challenge

Flight Time
Hanging Out in the Clouds

How this Learning Experience Meets the National Science Education Standards:

NSTA 5-8

Students develop abilities necessary to do scientific inquiry

- Students identify questions that can be measured through scientific inquiry.
- Students use appropriate tools and techniques to gather, analyze and interpret data.
- Students think critically and logically to make the relationships between evidence and explanations.
- Students recognize and analyze alternative explanations and predictions.
- Students communicate scientific procedures and explanations.
- Students use mathematics in all aspects of scientific inquiry.

Students develop abilities for technological design

- Students evaluate completed technological designs or products.

NCTM 6-8

- Students select and use appropriate statistical methods to analyze data.
- Students develop and evaluate inferences and predictions that are based on data.
- Students recognize and apply mathematics in contexts outside of mathematics.

ITEEA 6-9

Students develop an understanding of engineering design.

- Students learn that modeling, testing, evaluating, and modifying are used to transform ideas into practical solutions.

Students develop abilities to apply the design process.

- Students learn to apply a design process to solve problems in and beyond the laboratory-classroom.
- Students learn to make a product or system and document the solution.

Students develop abilities to assess the impact of products and systems.

- Students learn to design and use instruments to gather data.

NCTE K-12

- Students adjust their use of spoken, written and visual language to communicate effectively with a variety of audiences and for different purposes.

Objective:

Build a paper airplane. You can build whatever type of airplane you want. If you have never built a paper airplane, instructions for one type of plane are provided below. You may tape the wings together if desired.

Background:

This lesson introduces students to the art of designing an airplane through paper airplane constructions. The goal is that students will learn important aircraft design considerations and how engineers must modify their designs to achieve success. Students first follow directions to build several basic paper airplane models, after which they will then design their own paper airplane. They will also learn how engineers make models to test ideas and designs.

The process of building, testing and modifying designs to make them better helps and engineer perfect their design by learning from the mistakes of early designs. When designing an airplane, engineers often build small-scale models of the airplane to test how it will fly without building a large and expensive full-size aircraft. And, they experiment with many different designs to find the best one.

Usually paper airplanes are gliders. Gliders are planes without motors that ride on the air. The wings compress the air molecules underneath them, creating higher pressure under the wings and lower pressure on top of the wings. The difference in pressure is called lift and demonstrates Bernoulli's principle.

Adding features like flaps on the back of the wing or stabilizers or weight to the nose can change the flight direction or performance. A flap can turn the airplane, a heavy nose can cause the plane to dive and decreasing the nose weight can make the plane loop.

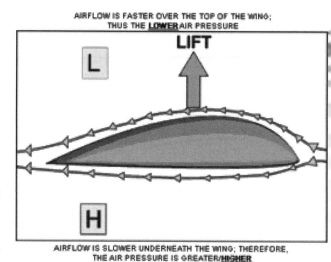

AIRFLOW IS FASTER OVER THE TOP OF THE WING; THUS THE LOWER AIR PRESSURE

LIFT

L

H

AIRFLOW IS SLOWER UNDERNEATH THE WING; THEREFORE, THE AIR PRESSURE IS GREATER/HIGHER

© Copyright NASA – www.nasa.gov

Materials

- Paper
- Tape (scotch and masking)
- Tape measure
- Stop watch or timer

Teacher Notes

- Flying the paper airplanes indoors has major advantages for the students. Not only is there no wind but they also won't crash into trees, land in water or other things that will destroy the plane. In addition, when you have a contest at the end of the lesson, it will ensure that everyone has the same flying conditions.
- Failure is important to success. When students first fold their planes, there is good chance that they won't fly well until adjusted.

- If the planes are diving and crashing, bend the back flaps or edge up a little. Try it again. If the plane still dives, bend the edge up a bit more.
- If the planes are climbing, stalling and then crashing back to earth, you probably have too much upward bend. Bend the edge down a bit.
- If the paper airplane goes to the right or to the left, adjust the rudder. Bend it in the opposite direction that the plane is going. If the plane veers to the right, bend the rudder to the left. Start bending in small increments and then try to fly the plane again.
- You may be able get more girls interested in this activity by providing colored paper to build the planes. Also, all students may enjoy decorating their planes for the competition.
- At the end of the lesson, have students think about the shape, wings, rudder, flaps or back edge of their airplane and what made them fly the best. Have a discussion about trial and error and remind them that engineers sometimes use trial and error to make the best design possible.

Safety Notes

Paper planes can have sharp edges and points that can injure someone. NEVER throw a paper airplane at another person, animal, or object that could be injured or damaged if you hit it. Paper planes can curve or change direction after they are launched, so make sure your flying area is clear.

Procedure

1. Instruct students to build a paper airplane and let them know they may scotch tape the wings together if desired. Students can build whatever type of airplane they are familiar with. If they have never built a paper airplane, instructions for one type of plane are provided on student sheet #1. Encourage the students to fold their favorite plane as it makes for great class discussions when charting the time aloft and distance traveled for different designs.
2. Once students have build their planes, have them test their design and record the distance and time aloft on the student sheet #2. Find a large indoor area such as a gym or hallway that the students can use to test their planes. Be sure to choose a starting line. To save time, one way to measure each student's flight distance is to have each student place their name on three pieces of masking tape. On each of three throws, the student will place one of the tape pieces on the floor horizontally aligned with the nose of the landed plane. After all the throws are completed, all measurements can be completed at one time by having a few students measure all pieces of tape at the same time and call out the names on the tape.

Paper Airplane Student Sheet #1

Build a paper airplane. You can build whatever type of airplane you want. If you have never built a paper airplane, instructions for one type of plane are provided below. You may tape the wings together if desired.

1. Fold paper in half and then lay it flat again. Fold the corners as shown.

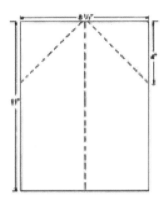

2. Fold again on the dotted line.

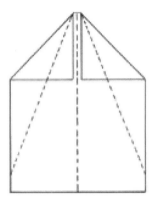

3. Fold away from you on the center line and make opposite folds on the dotted line

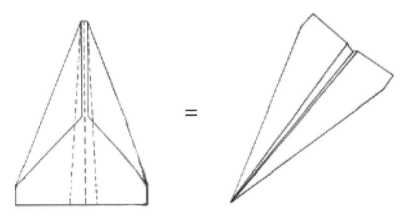

4. You may tapes the wings together if desired

5. Test your design! Record the distance and time aloft on the paper airplane student sheet #2.

Paper Airplane Student Sheet #2

ly your paper airplane three times and record the time aloft and distance traveled.

irplane Name: _____

Flight #	Where flown	Time aloft (seconds)	Distance flown (feet)
1			
2			
3			
Average			

f you could do it all over again, what would you change to make your plane fly further
r longer? Why?

_____

_____

_____

_____

_____

_____

_____

_____

_____

_____

Engineering Careers

Name _____

Across

2. What type of engineer designs the microchips that are in your computer, stereo, TV, etc?
4. What percentage of all engineering degrees went to women last year?
5. What type of engineer designs roller coasters?
10. What type of engineer designs running shoes?
11. What type of engineer designs iPods and other MP3 players so you can listen to your favorite music?
13. What type of engineer designed the bobsled course for the Winter Olympics?
14. What type of engineer ensures that we have clean drinking water?
15. Jimmy Carter, our 39th president was an engineer. What kind of engineer was he?
16. What type of engineer invented bubble gum?
17. George Washington was considered a _____ engineer.

Down

1. What type of engineer designs golf balls?
3. What type of engineer controls the crowd at a theme or amusement park?
6. What type of engineer invented the ear thermometer?
7. What type of engineer may work in a lab studying the effects of corn grown indoors.
8. What type of engineer designs bicycles?
9. What type of engineer designs the robots that can go inside your body to find blood clots?
12. What type of engineer makes chocolate taste so good?

Engineering Careers

Across

2. What type of engineer designs the microchips that are in your computer, stereo, TV, etc? [ceramic]
4. What percentage of all engineering degrees went to women last year? [eighteen]
5. What type of engineer designs roller coasters? [structural]
10. What type of engineer designs running shoes? [biomedical]
11. What type of engineer designs iPods and other MP3 players so you can listen to your favorite music? [electrical]
13. What type of engineer designed the bobsled course for the Winter Olympics? [civil]
14. What type of engineer ensures that we have clean drinking water? [environmental]
15. Jimmy Carter, our 39th president was an engineer. What kind of engineer was he? [nuclear]

Down

1. What type of engineer designs golf balls? [aerospace]
3. What type of engineer controls the crowd at a theme or amusement park? [industrial]
6. What type of engineer invented the ear thermometer? [biomedical]
7. What type of engineer may work in a lab studying the effects of corn grown indoors. [agricultural]
8. What type of engineer designs bicycles? [mechanical]
9. What type of engineer designs the robots that can go inside your body to find blood clots? [biomedical]
12. What type of engineer makes chocolate taste so good? [food]

Types of Engineering Technology

Name _____

```
L A C I D E M O I B R C J M O P T I C S W J T H U
I P F G K R M V O M I N P H V B W O F E S K A D R
U E I C E L R A E A E F U L Z D D H D E O G U A R
F T R G C A B P N S R L K N W N T M E K R T I M
O R E C Q C Y J T U X C E A S E V O A H F N O Y C
Q O P O O I D D X M F E H C T G K C R M X A M V N
E L R M D M D A P M L A P I T N Y A I U P S O B U
C E O P X E H W Q X A V C I R E F N J G S T Y F
A U T U C H N E E Q R E M T N E O M E Q W U I J X
P M E T F C D T S Q E W I M U D C N N R V D V A S
S T C E I P U F O F N X N U P R U T I O R X E Y Y
O S T R P X P C R X E W I K I D I S U C R J T R M
R E I I U G W U W X G N N G X W Q N T R A I K B Q
E A O X W E L D I N G D G J R X A M G R A N V P X
A V N X C O N S T R U C T I O N U H B W I L Q N V
T Z D L A C I N A H C E M O R T C E L E E A Y F E
S N O I T A C I N U M M O C E L E T B G G F L E F
```

amtelceoonitiusncm	ancrlhocemetclaie	retp ifeoncorit	vnltnemronaie
tiacrlrthueca	leceritcno	roctinoucnts	mtnrunugiafac
veuotoitam	bmdaieiloc	aeasopcre	lasuritdni
toeremupl	mcaleihc	rpcutemo	nleearg
naeimr	imngin	copsti	egwdnil

This page may be photocopied for use in the classroom.

Types of Engineering Technology

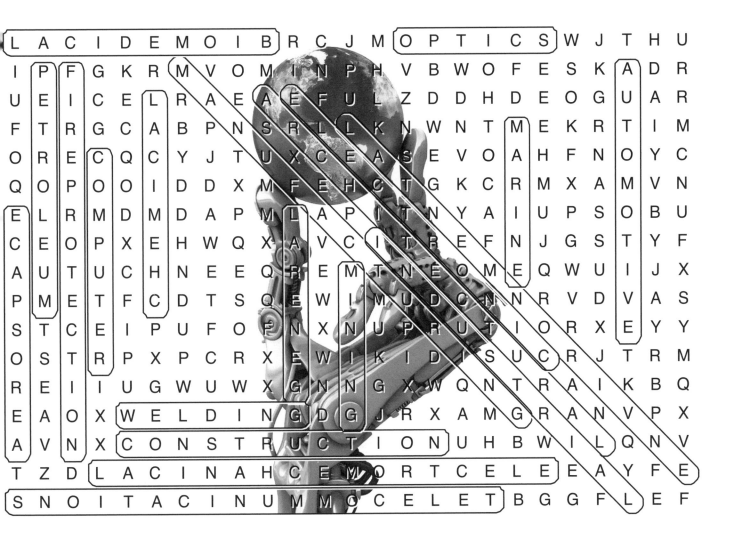

```
L A C I D E M O I B R C J M O P T I C S W J T H U
I P F G K R M V O M I N P H V B W O F E S K A D R
U E I C E L R A E A E F U L Z D D H D E O G U A R
F T R G C A B P N S R L L K N W N T M E K R T I M
O R E C Q C Y J T U X C E A S E V O A H F N O Y C
Q O P O O I D D X M F E H C T G K C R M X A M V N
E L R M D M D A P M L A P I T N Y A I U P S O B U
C E O P X E H W Q X A V C I T R E F N J G S T Y F
A U T U C H N E E Q R E M T N E O M E Q W U I J X
P M E T F C D T S Q E W I M U D C N N R D V A S
S T C E I P U F O F N X N U P R U T I O R X E Y Y
O S T R P X P C R X E W I K I D I S U C R J T R M
R E I I U G W U W X G N N G X W Q N T R A I K B Q
E A O X W E L D I N G D G J R X A M G R A N V P X
A V N X C O N S T R U C T I O N U H B W I L Q N V
T Z D L A C I N A H C E M O R T C E L E E A Y F E
S N O I T A C I N U M M O C E L E T B G G F L E F
```

amtelceoonitiusncm

tiacrlrthueca

veuotoitam

toeremupl

naeimr

ancrlhocemetclaie

leceritcno

bmdaieiloc

mcaleihc

imngin

retp ifeoncorit

roctinoucnts

aeasopcre

rpcutemo

copsti

vnltnemronaie

mtnrunugiafac

lasuritdni

nleearg

egwdnil

Biomedical Engineering

Biomedical Engineering

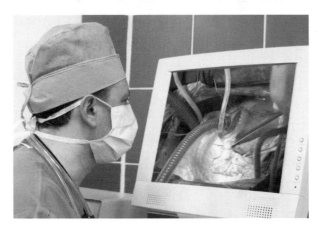

The objective of biomedical engineering is to enhance health care and quality of life by solving complex medical related problems using engineering principles. Those who specialize in this field want to serve the public, work with health care professionals, and interact with living systems. This broad field allows a large choice of sub-specialties. Many students say they chose biomedical engineering because it is people-oriented.

Imagine designing a medical device that appears to breathe life into someone or enhance and enable physical activity. Biomedical engineers invented the pacemaker and literally gave recipients the ability to once again perform physical activities, such as climbing a flight of stairs or walking around the block.

The biomedical engineering field changes rapidly. New technology is designed and fabricated every day. Biomedical engineers can expect a satisfying career with tremendous diversity and growth potential. The field includes many branches: biomechanical, bioelectrical, biochemical, rehabilitation, clinical and genetic engineering. There are also many sub-specialties within biomedical engineering such as surgical lasers, telemedicine, nuclear medicine, and clinical computer systems.

According to the Biomedical Engineering Society (BMES), examples of specialization include:

- Designing and constructing artificial organs and prosthetics (hearing aids, cardiac pacemakers, kidneys and hearts, blood oxygenators, synthetic blood vessels, joints, arms, and legs)
- Designing systems to automate patient monitoring (during surgery or in intensive care; and for healthy persons in unusual environments, such as astronauts in space or underwater divers at great depth)
- Designing blood chemistry sensors (potassium, sodium, O_2, CO_2, and pH)
- Designing advanced therapeutic instruments and surgical devices (laser systems for eye surgery, automated delivery of insulin, etc.)
- Applying expert systems and artificial intelligence to clinical decision-making (computer-based systems for diagnosing and monitoring diseases)
- Designing clinical laboratories (computerized analyzer for blood samples, cardiac catheterization laboratories, etc.)
- Designing, developing or improving medical imaging systems (ultrasound, computer-assisted tomography, magnetic resonance imaging (MRI), positron emission tomography (PET Scan), etc.)
- Implementing computer modeling of physiological systems (blood pressure control, renal function, visual and auditory nervous circuits, etc.)
- Designing biomaterials that won't be rejected by the body (mechanical, transport and biocompatibility properties of implantable artificial materials)
- Researching the biomechanics of injury and wound healing (gait analysis, application of growth factors, etc.)
- Designing and developing technique or applications for sports medicine (rehabilitation, external support devices, etc.)

Biomedical engineering is interdisciplinary and newer than most other types of engineering. Because of its interdisciplinary nature, it is possible to get a degree in mechanical, electrical, chemical, or materials engineering and still work as a biomedical engineer. In fact, 30 years ago, most biomedical engineers were trained in other forms of engineering because of the lack of available programs. Even 20 years ago, there were only a handful of programs, but today there are almost 40 accredited programs that students can attend. However, the opportunities increase if students consider another form of engineering such as mechanical, electrical, materials or chemical with an emphasis in biomedical engineering.

Some colleges of engineering may have their biomedical engineering department within the chemical, mechanical, or electrical engineering department. Typically, if a school has a program established this way, it will be smaller, and it may serve as more of an emphasis within other programs. Many students like this type of flexibility because it allows a much broader background. The important consideration when choosing this degree is that students attend an accredited program. If the program is not accredited, the option to continue their education in graduate school is almost nonexistent. To find accredited programs, visit the Accreditation Board for Engineering and Technology, Inc. (ABET) at www.abet.org.

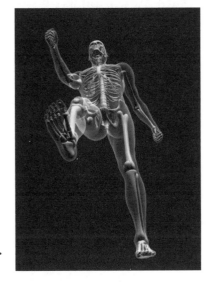

The demand for biomedical engineers and biomedical engineering technicians is higher than ever. Advancements in health care technology are exploding, and the U.S. Department of Labor predicts that this field is going to grow at a rate of 26 percent per year for the next six years, or almost double the rate for all other jobs combined! If this sounds astonishing, just watch the news – New advancements in medicine are being made almost every day.

Biomechanical Engineering

Biomechanical engineering or biomechanics is the specialty that sees the human body as a mechanical structure. These specialists investigate the motion of the human body, the stresses on bones and muscles, and the deformation of materials, such as artificial bones and joints. They might work for a company such as Nike to design a new running shoe after studying the impact caused by running. Biomechanical engineers may also design artificial limbs, joint replacements, or new materials to replace ligaments, tendons, or bones. An early development from a biomechanical engineer was the invention of the iron lung, which was an airtight respirator consisting of a metal tank that enclosed the entire body except for the head. It provided artificial respiration by contracting and expanding the walls of the chest.

A fascinating application of biomechanical engineering, according to Ellen Morrissey and Donald Lehr of the Nolan/Lehr Group, is the helmets used by hockey players. Though they appear to be made of a single piece of material, they are actually three different parts fitted together in an intricate, geometric configuration refined over the years for maximum energy absorption. (To test the helmet's ability to lessen impacts, manufacturers fit helmets with instrumental test heads and then drop them several meters. At the end of the drop, known as a "sudden deceleration," the testers examine the helmet's level of protection, and whether it has withstood impacts from 275- to 300 G-forces.) Besides providing protection, the helmet must also be light enough to keep the head cool, since hockey players are in constant motion and release a great deal of heat through their head. Lightness also allows players to accelerate at high speeds and then, since sudden stops square the effect of inertia, stop without tumbling off balance.

Bioelectrical Engineers

Biomedical engineering with an electrical emphasis is a popular choice among some students. Bioelectrical inventions are everywhere, from digital ear thermometers to sophisticated

MRI machines. Bioelectrical engineers are often responsible for developing machines that are used to diagnose and treat disease. An example of a bioelectrical development is the pacemaker, a device that senses irregular or arrested heart rhythms and restores the rhythms by giving electrical stimulation to the heart muscle. Bioelectrical engineers have also developed the electrocardiogram machine, which records, through electrodes placed on the skin, the beating of a heart. Bioelectrical engineers may design software or devices, such as electrophysiology cardiac monitors or telemedicine equipment, to aid doctors and hospitals. They may design devices to aid patients to self-monitor their conditions, or they may help a paraplegic become self-sufficient by designing an electrical system to regulate switches and appliances in the patient's house.

Bioelectrical engineers may also provide training for doctors and nurses on the effective use of such hospital equipment, and maintain the equipment as a field or customer service engineer.

Biochemical Engineering

Biochemical engineers concern themselves with body responses on a microscopic level. These engineers study the interactions between artificial materials that may cause negative reactions in the human body. They apply anatomy, biochemistry, and cellular mechanics to understand diseases and modes of intervention. Biochemical engineers developed woven acrylic artificial arteries to prevent blood clotting in artificial blood vessels. They also designed and constructed the artificial kidney for patients with incurable kidney disease.

Clinical Engineering

Clinical engineering is the branch of biomedical engineering that applies technology to health care in organizations such as hospitals and long-term care facilities; and for medical equipment vendors. Clinical engineers must understand the relationship of the equipment to the diagnosis, care and treatment of the patient.

High-risk assessments and the development of maintenance schedules and protocols are some of the other tasks they perform. They may also

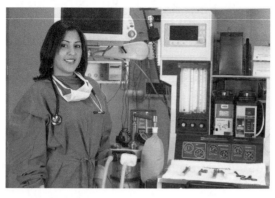

provide training for doctors, nurses, and other health professionals on the effective use of all medical equipment; and they may maintain the equipment. Clinical engineers may also evaluate equipment prior to purchase, test the equipment for safety, or modify existing hospital equipment. In addition, they may participate in accident or incident investigations.

Rehabilitation Engineering

Rehabilitation engineering is another popular specialty within biomedical engineering. Rehabilitation engineers participate in the research and development of technology to assist people with disabilities. According to the Biomedical Engineering Society, "Rehabilitation engineers enhance the capabilities and improve the quality of life for individuals with physical and cognitive impairments."

Assistive technology includes devices such as powered wheelchairs, talking computers, hearing aids, electronic talking devices, and any facilities that are modified, including grab bars for showers and restrooms. Recreational assistive technology, such as specially adapted skis and fishing poles, are other examples. If rehabilitation engineering interests you, watch the Special Olympics to see the assortment of assistive technology devices available. Imagine the feeling of power and accomplishment associated with giving a disabled person a new lease on life, providing a way to meet everyday life challenges successfully, and eliminating some of the challenges associated with having a disability in today's society.

A rehabilitation engineer may work on site with a person recently confined to a wheelchair to redesign the person's workspace; changes

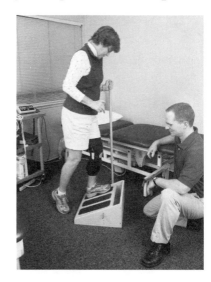

might include a desk that can be raised and lowered at the push of a button, wider doorways, and indoor ramps. A rehabilitation engineer may also redesign computer systems to assist people with cognitive or physical disabilities. One rehabilitation engineer designed a Braille keyboard so that blind people can type; another developed a system that enables people with no feeling below the waist to drive an automobile.

Biomedical Engineering Technology

Imagine being a biomedical technologist or technician (BMET) for a large hospital. All day, patients are admitted or diagnosed by hospital staff. The majority of the time, a diagnosis is made by using some type of electronic equipment. From simply the act of taking a patient's temperature using a digital thermometer to assessing arrhythmias using a cardiac monitor, biomedical engineering technologists and technicians are responsible for medical technology that enhances health care. BMETs are on the front line of health care, providing installation, design, manufacturing, training of hospital staff and personnel, and preventive maintenance for vital medical equipment. The work of the BMET ensures that all health care professionals can provide the care and treatment that patients need.

Biomedical engineering technologists and technicians focus primarily on medical equipment for hospitals and medical service providers. These positions require that the BMET work closely with physicians, nurses, therapists, hospital staff and other technical professionals to understand, assess, and make certain the diagnostic and therapeutic equipment and life-saving devices are operating within specifications. This field is similar to clinical engineering, and some BMET graduates will even be called clinical engineers. The difference is that clinical engineers, with a bachelor's degree in biomedical engineering, may be more involved in design, modification, and pre-purchase assessments whereas the BMETs may be more application-oriented and involved in installing, modifying, inspecting, testing, calibrating, or repairing the equipment. In addition, a BMET might be more likely to work in a hospital or clinical setting, while a BME would more usually work at a company.

BMETs must be also quick thinkers. If any equipment breaks down in the middle of a procedure and the patient's life is held in the balance, the BMET will be called in "STAT" to fix the problem. They may find themselves running through hospital corridors as precious minutes are ticking. Problems that arise could be as simple as a circuit breaker tripping in the operating room to a kidney dialysis machine malfunctioning in the middle of treatment. Whatever the case, this career requires fast thinking and good problem solving skills.

Currently, there are only a few ABET accredited biomedical engineering technology programs in the United States. However, many schools offer programs in electronic engineering technology with an emphasis in medical instrumentation, devices, or environments.

Examples of Biomedical Engineering and Biomedical Engineering Technology in Sports:

- May design systems for motion analysis and biomechanical analysis of injuries or stress patterns for athletic shoe design
- May design systems to analyze the human body while skiing or snowboarding to aid in injury prevention
- May research the motion of many sports to determine the requirements for product design and keeping people safe
- May design new suits or model a swimmer's performance on computer systems to analyze stroke capabilities
- May design systems to analyze the human body wearing a helmet for neck and spine injury prevention
- May research the impact aspects of many sports to determine the padding requirements

Boning up on Bones

Demonstrating the Strength of Materials

Time Required: 45-60 minutes

How this Learning Experience Meets the National Science Education Standards:

As a result of activities in grades 5-8, all students should develop:

Content Standard A: Science as Inquiry:

Abilities necessary to do scientific inquiry

- Identify questions that can be answered through scientific investigations.
- Design and conduct a scientific investigation.
- Use appropriate tools and techniques to gather, analyze and interpret data.
- Develop descriptions, explanations, predictions and models using evidence.
- Think critically and logically to make the relationships between evidence and explanations.
- Recognize and analyze alternative explanations and predictions.
- Communicate scientific procedures and explanations.
- Use mathematics in all aspects of scientific inquiry.

Understanding Scientific Inquiry

- Different kinds of questions suggest different kinds of scientific investigations.
- Mathematics is important in all aspects of scientific inquiry.
- Technology used to gather data enhances accuracy and allows scientists to analyze and quantify results of investigations.
- Scientific explanations emphasize evidence, have logically consistent arguments, and use scientific principles, models and theories.
- Scientific investigations sometimes result in new ideas and phenomena for study, generate new methods or procedures for an investigation, or develop new technologies to improve the collection of data.

How this learning experience meets the National Standards for Technological Literacy:

- Standard 1. Students will develop an understanding of the characteristics and scope of technology.
- Standard 2. Students will develop an understanding of the core concepts of technology.
- Standard 9. Students will develop an understanding of engineering design.
- Standard 13. Students will develop the abilities to assess the impact of products and systems.

Overview:

In this activity, students will learn about bone strength by building models with different hard outer layers and testing them to failure.

Background:

Human beings are vertebrates, which make up only three percent of animals. Vertebrates are animals that have an internal skeleton made of bones and include not only mammals but fish, amphibians, reptiles, birds, primates, rodents and marsupials. The skeletal system's star is the spinal cord since it forms the structure of the human body, and also contains and protects the central nervous system. The skeleton is made of calcified connective tissue, or bones. Humans have about 206 bones that make up body shape and protect internal organs. Bones, through the marrow inside, produce blood cells, allow the body to move, store minerals and support the body.

Bones contain more calcium than any other part of the body, and are actually not solid but porous Each bone is made up of some combination of two layers: an inner layer that is spongy, and an outer layer of compact bone that is hard. Longer bones such as those in arms or legs tend to be more dense, while the smaller bones of the wrist and ankles are spongier. Bones begin to develop before birth as cartilage, which is flexible. Over the first 20 years of life, bones harden through a process called ossification that replaces the cartilage with calcium deposits and collagen.

Because bones are made up of living cells, they can repair themselves after a break. They can also be transplanted and donated.

Teacher Notes:

In this activity, students will explore bone strength by testing two types of model bones consisting of rolled paper of different weights and stiffness. The bones will be 11 inches (28 cm) long, a little longer than the radius of a forearm bone in an average-sized woman. The bones will be tested for strength by suspending a load from the middle.

Safety Notes:

During testing have one student monitoring the pail to try to catch it before it falls.

Getting Started:

Set up the testing area by placing two desks or tables so there is a 4 inch (10.2 cm) gap between the desktops.

Materials needed per team/pair of students:

- 1 sheet 8.5"x11" copy paper, 20-24#
- 1 sheet 8.5"x11" cardstock paper, 67-90#
- Scissors
- Ruler
- Masking tape, 6 inches (15 cm) per bone; 12 inches (30 cm) per team

Materials needed for test station:

- Large plastic paint bucket with handle
- Duct tape
- 1-2 feet link chain (available at hardware store)

- 2 S-type or other hooks to attach pail and model to chain
- Mass Weights, 1 kg and greater, or other suitable load material
- Two desks or tables for testing 'bones'; must have clearance for pail to hang freely

Procedure:

1. Instruct students to build two model bones, one of each weight of paper and each 11 inches (28 cm) long. They may use up to a maximum of one 8.5"x11" sheet of paper and 6 inches (15 cm) of masking tape for each model.

2. To set up the testing station, move two tables or desks close together so that the gap between the flat surfaces is about 4 inches (10.2 cm). Place the bone to be tested over the gap with equal overlap on either side. Secure each end to the table using a 1 inch (2.5 cm) long piece of duct tape.

3. For testing, attach one of the hooks to each end of the chain. Put one hook over the middle of the bone span and attach the other to the handle of the plastic paint bucket. The bucket should swing freely between the desks and be suspended above the floor.

4. Start with a 1 kg (2.2 lbs) load in the pail. Add weight in any desired increment until the model bone fails. The last mass successfully supported by the model before it failed is the total load it can support. Ask students to record their final readings on the student data sheet.

5. As a class, collect all values of the results and calculate the mean mass supported by each type of bone.

6. What difference did the paper weight make in the amount of weight each bone will support? How does this relate to real human bones? (The amount of calcium in our bones is a big factor in bone hardness.)

Boning up on Bones
Student Sheet

Team members:

_____

_____

_____

Procedure:

1. Gather materials; for each group: 1 piece each of copy paper and cardstock paper, scissors, 12 inches (30.5 cm) of masking tape and a ruler. Your task is to design two different models (one of each type of paper provided) of an 11 inch (28 cm) long bone.

2. You may use up to the whole sheet of paper for each model, but you do not have to use all. Secure your final design with tape. Remember you only have 6 inches (15 cm) of tape to use for each model.

3. Take your completed bones to the testing station. You will begin with a 1 kg load. Incremental weights will be added until your bone fails by bending or breaking and causing the pail to fall. Record the LAST SUCCESSFULLY HELD MASS (the one before the failure) in the data table below.

Data Collection:

Type of Paper	Copy (20-24#)	Cardstock (65-110#)
Size of Paper (How much did you use?)		
Maximum Mass Supported		

This page may be photcopied for use in the classroom.

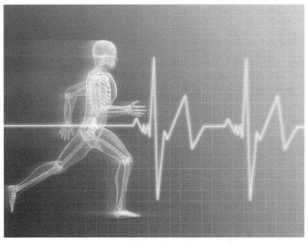

Keep it Moving

Unclogging a clogged artery

Time Required: 45-60 minutes

How this learning experience meets the national science education standards:

Content Standard A: Science as Inquiry: As a result of activities in grades 5-8, all students should develop:

Abilities necessary to do scientific inquiry
* Identify questions that can be answered through scientific investigations.
* Design and conduct a scientific investigation.
* Use appropriate tools and techniques to gather, analyze and interpret data.
* Develop descriptions, explanations, predictions and models using evidence.
* Think critically and logically to make the relationships between evidence and explanations.
* Recognize and analyze alternative explanations and predictions.
* Communicate scientific procedures and explanations.
* Use mathematics in all aspects of scientific inquiry.

Understanding Scientific Inquiry
* Different kinds of questions suggest different kinds of scientific investigations.
* Current scientific knowledge and understanding guide scientific investigations.
* Mathematics is important in all aspects of scientific inquiry.
* Technology used to gather data enhances accuracy and allows scientists to analyze and quantify results of investigations.
* Scientific explanations emphasize evidence, have logically consistent arguments, and use scientific principles, models and theories.
* Science advances through legitimate skepticism.
* Scientific investigations sometimes result in new ideas and phenomena for study, generate new methods or procedures for an investigation, or develop new technologies to improve the collection of data.

Content Standard E: Science and Technology: As a result of activities in grades 5-8, all students should develop:

Abilities of technological design
* Identify appropriate problems for technological design.
* Design a solution or a product.

- Implement a proposed design.
- Evaluate completed technological designs or products.
- Communicate the process of technological design.

Understanding about science and technology
- Scientific inquiry and technological design have similarities and differences. Scientists propose explanations for questions about the natural world, and engineers propose solutions relating to human problems, needs, and aspirations. Technological solutions are temporary; technologies exist within nature and so they cannot contravene physical or biological principles; technological solutions have side effects; and technologies cost, carry risks, and provide benefits.
- Science and technology are reciprocal. Science helps drive technology, as it addresses questions that demand more sophisticated instruments and provides principles for better instrumentation and technique. Technology is essential to science, because it provides instruments and techniques that enable observations of objects and phenomena that are otherwise unobservable due to factors such as quantity, distance, location, size, and speed. Technology also provides tools for investigations, inquiry, and analysis.
- Perfectly designed solutions do not exist. All technological solutions have trade-offs, such as safety, cost, efficiency, and appearance. Engineers often build in back-up systems to provide safety. Risk is part of living in a highly technological world. Reducing risk often results in new technology.
- Technological designs have constraints. Some constraints are unavoidable, for example, properties of materials, or effects of weather and friction; other constraints limit choices in the design, for example, environmental protection, human safety, and aesthetics.
- Technological solutions have intended benefits and unintended consequences. Some consequences can be predicted, others cannot.

Content Standard C: Life Science: As a result of their activities in grades 5-8, all students should develop understanding of:
Structure and function in living systems
- The human organism has systems for digestion, respiration, reproduction, circulation, excretion, movement, control, and coordination, and for protection from disease. These systems interact with one another.
- Disease is a breakdown in structures or functions of an organism. Some diseases are the result of intrinsic failures of the system. Others are the result of damage by infection by other organisms.

CONTENT STANDARD G:
As a result of activities in grades 5-8, all students should develop understanding of:
Nature of Science
- Scientists formulate and test their explanations of nature using observation, experiments, and theoretical and mathematical models. Although all scientific ideas are tentative and subject to change and improvement in principle, for most major ideas in science, there is much experimental and observational confirmation. Those ideas are not likely to change greatly in the future. Scientists do and have changed their ideas about nature when they encounter new experimental evidence that does not match their existing explanations.

How this learning experience meets the National Standards for Technological Literacy:
- Standard 1. Students will develop an understanding of the characteristics and scope of technology.
- Standard 2. Students will develop an understanding of the core concepts of technology.
- Standard 3. Students will develop an understanding of the relationships among technologies and the connections between technology and other fields of study.
- Standard 4. Students will develop an understanding of the cultural, social, economic, and political effects of technology

- Standard 6. Students will develop an understanding of the role of society in the development and use of technology.
- Standard 8. Students will develop an understanding of the attributes of design.
- Standard 9. Students will develop an understanding of engineering design.
- Standard 10. Students will develop an understanding of the role of troubleshooting, research and development, invention and innovation, and experimentation in problem solving.
- Standard 13. Students will develop the abilities to assess the impact of products and systems.

Overview:
In this activity, students will explore various methods to open blocked arteries.

Background:
Our body's circulatory system is comprised of three parts: pulmonary (lungs), coronary (heart) and systemic (the rest of the body). We each have about five liters of blood that travels continually throughout the system, relying on the heart to pump the blood. These systems of blood vessels, made up of arteries (largest), veins and capillaries (smallest), send oxygen and nutrients to all body tissues. Over time fatty plaques can build up in arteries, slowing or blocking the flow of blood. This condition, called atherosclerosis, occurs naturally but can be made worse by unhealthy lifestyle choices such as eating a high fat diet, lack of exercise and smoking. Atherosclerosis can cause damage or even death to the heart by slowing or stopping blood flow. Cardiovascular physicians work to help patients clear blockages and restrictions in arteries through lifestyle changes, medication and/or surgery.

There are three invasive measures cardiac surgeons use to treat blocked arteries: balloon angioplasty, insertion of a stent and bypass surgery. In both balloon angioplasty and stent insertion, a tiny hollow tube called a catheter is inserted into an artery. Typically, the catheter is inserted through an incision in the groin area and threaded up through arteries to the heart. With balloon angioplasty, a balloon inflated in the artery through the catheter compresses the plaque against the artery wall which widens it for increased blood flow. The balloon is then removed. A stent is a metal tube that is also inserted via a catheter and inflated; however a stent remains in the artery to hold the artery open. Coronary bypass surgery is used to reroute the blood flow around clogged arteries by attaching, or grafting, veins from other parts of the body (typically the leg) to coronary arteries.

Teacher Notes:
1. Prepare in advance the model arteries by cutting the tubing and filling with shortening. Cut 4 inch (12.7 cm) long sections of $\frac{1}{2}$ to 1 inch diameter clear plastic tubing, found in hardware stores. Each team will need two pieces for models and one clear piece of tubing. To make the models, insert one end of the tubing into the shortening to load; use a toothpick or wooden coffee stir stick to distribute inside tube and create full or partial "blockage."
2. It's not important that every model be exactly the same; the important concept is developing methods to minimize the restriction of water flow in the tube.

Safety Notes:
Using a foil baking pan to test flow will keep water contained.

Getting Started:
1. Prepare materials in advance for each team. Assemble in foil pan for easy distribution.
2. Depending on student levels, prior instruction in methods to treat blocked arteries may be helpful. See Background for more information.

Materials needed per team of 3-4 students:
- Rectangular foil baking pan or similar container to conduct water testing
- 2 artery models (see teacher notes; 4 inch long clear plastic tubing with shortening inside)
- 4 inch (12.7 cm) long piece of clear plastic tubing

- 3 Pipe cleaners
- 3 Plastic coffee stirrers, cut into 1 to 2 inch pieces
- Toothpicks
- Long balloon, such as those used to twist into animal shapes
- Scissors
- Stopwatch or clock or watch with second hand
- 16.9 oz (500 ml) plastic bottle, empty
- Water (or access to it)
- Student handout

Procedure:

1. Examine the two artery models and estimate the amount of blockage in each. This can be done by holding the tube at an angle and looking through it. Record observation on the student handout.
2. Fill the bottle with water. Lean the cleared tube against the wall of the pan at about a 45 degree angle. With one team member acting as timekeeper, hold the tube in place and pour the water into the tube. Time how long it takes for the entire bottle of water to pass through; record your data. This is your control.
3. Repeat step two with both model arteries. You will have to refill the bottle for each trial and you may need to empty the pan in between trials. Record all data.
4. Using the available materials, design a system to clear or minimize the blockage in each of the model arteries. List your materials and draw a picture of each solution. Record observed blockage estimate after implementing your solution on student handout.
5. Test your solutions by conducting the water test from step two. Record and compare your flow times on the student handout.
6. Participate in a class discussion about results and designs. Was there a consistent design that was successful or not?

Keep it Moving
Student Sheet

Team members:

_____

_____

_____

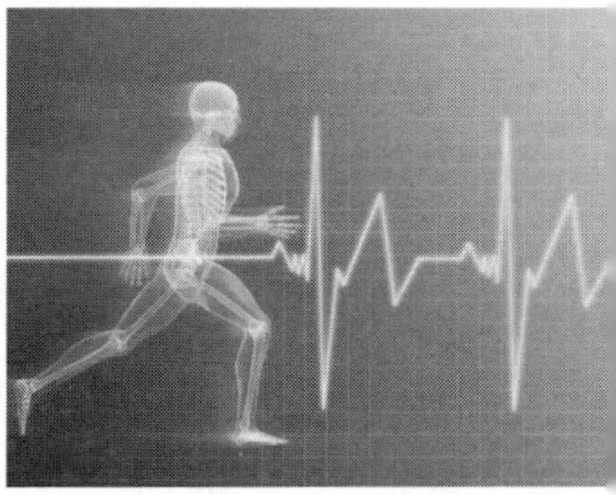

Data Table			
	Clear Artery	**Artery Model 1**	**Artery Model 2**
Initial Blockage Amount	No blockage	No blockage Little blockage Half blocked Mostly blocked Completely blocked	No blockage Little blockage Half blocked Mostly blocked Completely blocked
First Water Flow Trial	_____ seconds	_____ seconds	_____ seconds
Improved Blockage Amount		No blockage Little blockage Half blocked Mostly blocked Completely blocked	No blockage Little blockage Half blocked Mostly blocked Completely blocked
Second Water Flow Trial		_____ seconds	_____ seconds

List materials and sketch solution for artery model 1:

List materials and sketch solution for artery model 2:

This page may be photcopied for use in the classroom.

Prosthetic Hand
A Gripping Problem

How this learning experience meets the national science education standards:

Content Standard A: Science as Inquiry: As a result of activities in grades 5-8, all students should develop:

Abilities necessary to do scientific inquiry
- Identify questions that can be answered through scientific investigations.
- Design and conduct a scientific investigation.
- Use appropriate tools and techniques to gather, analyze and interpret data.
- Develop descriptions, explanations, predictions and models using evidence.
- Think critically and logically to make the relationships between evidence and explanations.
- Recognize and analyze alternative explanations and predictions.
- Communicate scientific procedures and explanations.

Understanding Scientific Inquiry
- Different kinds of questions suggest different kinds of scientific investigations.
- Current scientific knowledge and understanding guide scientific investigations.
- Mathematics is important in all aspects of scientific inquiry.
- Technology used to gather data enhances accuracy and allows scientists to analyze and quantify results of investigations.
- Scientific explanations emphasize evidence, have logically consistent arguments, and use scientific principles, models and theories.
- Science advances through legitimate skepticism.
- Scientific investigations sometimes result in new ideas and phenomena for study, generate new methods or procedures for an investigation, or develop new technologies to improve the collection of data.

Content Standard E: Science and Technology: As a result of activities in grades 5-8, all students should develop:

Abilities of technological design
- Identify appropriate problems for technological design.
- Design a solution or a product.
- Implement a proposed design.
- Evaluate completed technological designs or products.
- Communicate the process of technological design.

Understanding about science and technology
- Scientific inquiry and technological design have similarities and differences. Scientists propose explanations for questions about the natural world, and engineers propose solutions relating to human problems, needs, and aspirations. Technological solutions are temporary; technologies exist within nature and so they cannot contravene physical or biological principles; technological solutions have side effects; and technologies cost, carry risks, and provide benefits.
- Science and technology are reciprocal. Science helps drive technology, as it addresses questions that demand more sophisticated instruments and provides principles for better instrumentation and technique. Technology is essential to science, because it provides instruments and techniques that enable observations of objects and phenomena that are otherwise unobservable due to factors such as quantity, distance, location, size, and speed. Technology also provides tools for investigations, inquiry, and analysis.
- Perfectly designed solutions do not exist. All technological solutions have trade-offs, such as safety, cost, efficiency, and appearance. Engineers often build in back-up systems to provide safety. Risk is part of living in a highly technological world. Reducing risk often results in new technology.
- Technological designs have constraints. Some constraints are unavoidable, for example, properties of materials, or effects of weather and friction; other constraints limit choices in the design, for example, environmental protection, human safety, and aesthetics.
- Technological solutions have intended benefits and unintended consequences. Some consequences can be predicted, others cannot.

Content Standard C: Life Science: As a result of their activities in grades 5-8, all students should develop understanding of:

Structure and function in living systems
- The human organism has systems for digestion, respiration, reproduction, circulation, excretion, movement, control, and coordination, and for protection from disease. These systems interact with one another.
- Disease is a breakdown in structures or functions of an organism. Some diseases are the result of intrinsic failures of the system. Others are the result of damage by infection by other organisms.

CONTENT STANDARD G:
As a result of activities in grades 5-8, all students should develop understanding of:

Nature of Science
- Scientists formulate and test their explanations of nature using observation, experiments, and theoretical and mathematical models. Although all scientific ideas are tentative and subject to change and improvement in principle, for most major ideas in science, there is much experimental and observational confirmation. Those ideas are not likely to change greatly in the future. Scientists do and have changed their ideas about nature when they encounter new experimental evidence that does not match their existing explanations.

Overview:

Using only the materials given, design a 3-finger prosthetic hand that can pick up a wad of paper.
Time Required: 40-50 minutes

Background:

It has been said that the most positive aspect of utilizing design technology projects is that students and their teachers begin to look at problems and issues from multiple points of view and in relationship to a variety of contexts. One problem may even create another problem and there are usually several different solutions to each problem.

Students also learn that design technology, or engineering design, like life itself, is an endless process of solving problems. In solving any problem, people take the same steps as the ones that students will utilize in their design technology experiences:

- Stating the problem clearly.
- Collecting information.
- Developing possible solutions.
- Selecting the best solutions.
- Implementing the solution.
- Evaluating the solution.
- Making the needed changes and improving the solution.
- Communicating their findings.

The action of solving problems also opens up the creative process for students, thus enhancing the engagement of students in the classroom learning. Reports indicate that when students are building and creating things in the classroom, the engagement level is consistently intense. It does not allow a student to simply sit back and wait to be told what to do, but instead requires that the student create, test, and evaluate for themselves. This in turn leads to genuine decision making, which should be an integral part of the entire curriculum. The goal of problem solving is to educate students to be able to use the scientific process no matter what the problem is that they encounter.

Teacher Notes:

Hydraulics are normally used to lift heavy loads that would otherwise seem impossible. Because hydraulics use water in the syringes and tubes for pressure, be sure you have a bucket of water available for students to fill their syringes. You may want to demonstrate how to fill the syringes with as few air bubbles as possible. Food color in the water can make the activity more visually interesting. Have towels available.

You can extend this challenge by having the fingers pick up objects with more mass or more width. You can also challenge students to pick up the paper by scooping or by pinching from the top.

While students are testing their hands, instruct them to think about different ways they may modify their designs to increase performance. This portion of the activity can be as long or short as you choose. You can have the students sketch their modifications (to scale) or you can simply let students perform open inquiry/exploration to find the answers or new solutions.

To complete the activity, students are going to guide their teammates to pick up the wad of paper as if the hand was robotic and needed instructional code similar to computer instructions. One member of the team will be blindfolded and listen to instructions. Each group that is successful should win a prize. Be sure to point out that efficiency and accuracy is critical.

Safety Notes:

Students will need ample space to not only construct but test their hands. Be certain that there are no dangerous obstacles in the work area. Be careful with scissors and have a first aid kit available for class use.

Materials Needed

- 2-3 small storage tubs
- 3" x 3" or larger note pads

Materials Needed per Team

- 2 syringes
- 3 paperclips
- 10 straws (2 sizes)
- 10 popsicle sticks
- 1 meter of string
- 3 pipe cleaners
- 2 ft of tubing
- 3 index cards
- 1 meter of tape
- 5 rubber bands
- scissors
- ruler

Engineering Constraints

- The hand must be made from only the approved materials.
- The hand cannot be taped or attached to the table in any way.
- The hand must use hydraulics to pick up the paper.

Each Team Must Perform According to These Guidelines:

- All members of the team must participate.
- The members of the team must come to a consensus on the design and construction of the hand.
- The hand design and construction must be completed within the time frame stated.
- The team's hand must be tested in front of the class, passing the same test as all other hands.

Procedure:

1. Arrange students into cooperative teams; assign tasks within the groups as appropriate.
2. Provide each group with the design challenge.
3. Have materials managers gather the needed materials.
4. Initiate the learning experience.
5. Following the time limit, have each team designate a listener (hand operator) and a controller.
6. Blindfold the listener and have the controller give instructions to pick up one wad of paper from the tub.
7. Facilitate a discussion and develop concepts as needed.
8. Award prizes accordingly.

Prosthetic Hand
Student Sheet

Using only the materials given, design a 3-finger prosthetic hand that can pick up a wad of paper.

Materials - Every team should have the following materials:

- 2 syringes
- 2 ft of tubing
- 3 paperclips
- 5 straws (2 sizes of each)
- 1 meter of tape
- 10 popsicle sticks
- 5 rubber bands
- 1 meter of string
- 3 index cards
- 3 pipe cleaners

Engineering Constraints
- The hand must be made from only the approved materials.
- The hand cannot be taped or attached to the table in any way.
- The hand must use hydraulics to pick up the paper.

Your Team Must Perform According to These Guidelines:
- All members of the team must participate.
- The members of the team must come to a consensus on the design and construction of the hand.
- The hand design and construction must be completed within the timeframe stated.
- The team's hand must be tested in front of the class, passing the same test as all other hands.

Gut Reaction

Dealing with Stomach Acid

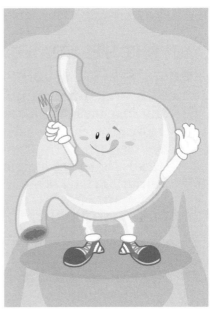

Time Required: 60-75 minutes for up to four samples

How this learning experience meets the national science education standards:

Content Standard A: Science as Inquiry: As a result of activities in grades 5-8, all students should develop:

Abilities necessary to do scientific inquiry
- Identify questions that can be answered through scientific investigations.
- Design and conduct a scientific investigation.
- Use appropriate tools and techniques to gather, analyze and interpret data.
- Develop descriptions, explanations, predictions and models using evidence.
- Think critically and logically to make the relationships between evidence and explanations.
- Recognize and analyze alternative explanations and predictions.
- Communicate scientific procedures and explanations.
- Use mathematics in all aspects of scientific inquiry.

Understanding Scientific Inquiry
- Different kinds of questions suggest different kinds of scientific investigations.
- Current scientific knowledge and understanding guide scientific investigations.
- Mathematics is important in all aspects of scientific inquiry.
- Technology used to gather data enhances accuracy and allows scientists to analyze and quantify results of investigations.
- Scientific explanations emphasize evidence, have logically consistent arguments, and use scientific principles, models and theories.
- Science advances through legitimate skepticism.
- Scientific investigations sometimes result in new ideas and phenomena for study, generate new methods or procedures for an investigation, or develop new technologies to improve the collection of data.

CONTENT STANDARD B: Physical Science: As a result of their activities in grades 5-8, all students should develop an understanding of:

Properties and changes of properties in matter

- Substances react chemically in characteristic ways with other substances to form new substances (compounds) with different characteristic properties. In chemical reactions, the total mass is conserved. Substances often are placed in categories or groups if they react in similar ways; metals is an example of such a group.

CONTENT STANDARD C: Life Science: As a result of their activities in grades 5-8, all students should develop understanding of:

Structure and function in living systems

- The human organism has systems for digestion, respiration, reproduction, circulation, excretion, movement, control, and coordination, and for protection from disease. These systems interact with one another.
- Disease is a breakdown in structures or functions of an organism. Some diseases are the result of intrinsic failures of the system. Others are the result of damage by infection by other organisms.

Content Standard E: Science and Technology: As a result of activities in grades 5-8, all students should develop:

Abilities of technological design

- Identify appropriate problems for technological design.
- Design a solution or a product.
- Implement a proposed design.
- Evaluate completed technological designs or products.
- Communicate the process of technological design. Understanding about science and technology
- Scientific inquiry and technological design have similarities and differences. Scientists propose explanations for questions about the natural world, and engineers propose solutions relating to human problems, needs, and aspirations. Technological solutions are temporary; technologies exist within nature and so they cannot contravene physical or biological principles; technological solutions have side effects; and technologies cost, carry risks, and provide benefits.
- Science and technology are reciprocal. Science helps drive technology, as it addresses questions that demand more sophisticated instruments and provides principles for better instrumentation and technique. Technology is essential to science, because it provides instruments and techniques that enable observations of objects and phenomena that are otherwise unobservable due to factors such as quantity, distance, location, size, and speed. Technology also provides tools for investigations, inquiry, and analysis.
- Perfectly designed solutions do not exist. All technological solutions have trade-offs, such as safety, cost, efficiency, and appearance. Engineers often build in back-up systems to provide safety. Risk is part of living in a highly technological world. Reducing risk often results in new technology.
- Technological designs have constraints. Some constraints are unavoidable, for example, properties of materials, or effects of weather and friction; other constraints limit choices in the design, for example, environmental protection, human safety, and aesthetics.
- Technological solutions have intended benefits and unintended consequences. Some consequences can be predicted, others cannot.

How this learning experience meets the National Standards for Technological Literacy:

- Standard 4. Students will develop an understanding of the cultural, social, economic, and political effects of technology.
- Standard 9. Students will develop an understanding of engineering design.
- Standard 10. Students will develop an understanding of the role of troubleshooting, research and development, invention and innovation, and experimentation in problem solving.
- Standard 13. Students will develop the abilities to assess the impact of products and systems.

Overview:

In this activity, students will explore different aspects of swallowed medicine delivery, one of the engineering aspects of developing new medications.

Background:

When scientists work on new medicines to treat different medical conditions, two important factors they must consider are how to deliver it to best treat the condition being targeted, and how to keep the patient as safe and comfortable as possible. Often, the method of delivery depends on which body system the medicine works through. For example, chemotherapy drugs are often administered directly into a vein through an intravenous system. Some medicines get into the body through a transdermal method, or one that works through the skin. When medicines come in pill form and are swallowed, they travel directly to the stomach. If the medicine is harsh, it can hurt the stomach or esophagus (the tube from your mouth to your stomach). Often, the scientists and engineers that develop the medicine will design ways to make it taste better, protect the stomach through a coating, or delay or time the release of the medicine.

Nearly everyone has experienced stomach pain at some point. Stomach pain can be as simple as indigestion or gas buildup, to more serious conditions such as ulcers or chronic acid reflux. Our stomachs are designed to be the first step in digesting food by breaking it down using gastric acid. A healthy stomach has an acidity level, known as pH, between 1 and 3. The inside of the stomach itself is protected by a mucous lining. Gastric ulcers, or those in the stomach, are small holes or erosions that can be caused by excess acid, injury, or the chronic use of anti-inflammatory medicine. Cigarettes also can cause gastric ulcers. Some stomach pains are not in the stomach at all, but rather in the upper part of the digestive system called the esophagus. The pH of the esophagus is higher, or less acidic, than the stomach. When acid from the stomach gets through the small flap (sphincter) separating it from the esophagus, the acid level there increases. This can cause the pain of heartburn, regurgitation and GERD (gastroesophageal reflux disease).

There are many medicines on the market, both prescription and over the counter, which address these issues of stomach and digestive tract pain. They are designed to do various things such as neutralizing excess acid, relieving gas buildup, or even preventing the production of excess acid. Proton pump inhibitors (PPI), for example, work by blocking acid production in the stomach. They are commonly recommended for acid reflux and ulcers, among other conditions. Antacids and other gastrointestinal medications address the issues of indigestion and excess gas. Some of these medications are long acting, which means they take a while to work, while others act immediately. Some are swallowed whole while others must be chewed before swallowing. In this activity, students will explore the impact on acid reduction when compared with the type of delivery system.

Teacher Notes:

A variety of samples are recommended for this activity. Specific brands are not necessary; rather a selection of different brands and generic over the counter antacids will provide a wider experience. Try to get some samples where chewing is recommended as well as some that may be swallowed whole. Make the acid solution (1 part vinegar to 2 parts water; resulting pH of about 2) ahead of time for easy distribution.

Safety Notes:

1. Student groups should be closely supervised with the medications.

2. Keep group sizes small to ensure engagement of all participants.
3. Safety glasses should be worn during this exercise.

Getting Started:
1. Place two of each type of medicine in small snack size zipped bags. Label each bag with the name of the medicine being tested. If using any liquid antacids, measure recommended dose into small condiment cup (only one sample needed of liquids).
2. Students should be familiar with reading pH test strips.
3. Ph color code chart is available online: http://en.wikipedia.org/wiki/PH_indicator
4. Provide necessary background information for students:

"Today we will explore how some stomach acid medications work. Scientists and engineers who develop these medicines need to design them to work effectively and safely in the stomach. All of these medicines are designed to reduce the pain of too much stomach acid. Acids are chemicals that are corrosive and have a low pH. Stomach acid is normal and desired; as it helps to break down the food we eat in order to digest it. However, if too much acid is made, or it goes back up into our esophagus, it can cause irritation, pain and even more serious conditions. Antacids, the type of medicine we will be studying, are made to decrease or neutralize stomach acid. We will be exploring whether the way we take an antacid results in a different effectiveness in neutralizing stomach acid."

Materials needed per team of 2-3 students:
- White Vinegar ($^1/_4$ cup per plastic cup)
- Water ($^1/_2$ cup per plastic cup)
- Measuring cups
- 9 oz clear plastic cups, 2 for each type of antacid to be tested
- A variety of antacids, such as Tums, Mylanta, Maalox, Gas-X, generic versions of same (2 doses of each)
- Small condiment cups, if using any liquid antacids
- Measuring spoons, if using any liquid antacids
- Small snack size Ziploc bags
- Rubber mallets or other implements to crush tablet in zip bag
- pH test strips, 4 for each sample being tested
- pH color code chart
- Stopwatch or clock with second hand
- Student handout

Procedure:
1. For each antacid being tested, each team of students receives two 9 oz plastic cups, half full of the vinegar/water solution (acid), and a baggie with two samples in it (or one condiment cup with a dose of liquid antacid). The other materials should be readily available to the team.
2. Select one team member to be the timekeeper. This person will note and record time to ensure pH measurements are taken at the correct intervals.
3. First, using one pH strip, measure and record on the student handout the pH of the vinegar/ water solutions. To do this, dip the end of the strip into the solution. Compare the color of the wet end of the strip to the pH color chart provided; record results. One end can be used for one cup, the other end for the other cup.
4. Remove one antacid sample from the Ziploc bag; place it in the first cup. Note time.

5. Using the rubber mallet or other tool, push down on the remaining tablet in the Ziploc bag to break it. Keep pushing on it until the tablet in crushed.

6. Pour the crushed tablet into the second cup. Note the time.

7. Using a pH test strip, measure the pH after five minutes for each solution. Record the results.

8. Note observations on the student handout: has the color of the solution changed? Has the entire tablet dissolved?

9. Repeat steps 6 and 7 after another five minutes (10 minutes total).

10. Repeat steps 6 and 7 after another five minutes (15 minutes total). This will be your final pH reading of the solution.

11. Repeat process with each antacid until finished. Record all data on handout.

12. After all testing is completed, report results to the teacher to record on the board or chart paper. Were there any differences in acid neutralization between whole and crushed tablets of the same type? Did crushed tablets overall neutralize the acid faster, or more than those tested whole? How did the teams' results compare with one another? Finally, how did the tests support (or not) the directions for each medicine?

Gut Reaction: Testing Stomach Acid Solutions
Student Handout

	Antacid	Crushed or Whole	Initial pH (before adding antacid)	pH after five minutes	pH after ten minutes	pH after 15 minutes (final pH)	Total Change in pH
1							
2							
3							
4							
5							
6							
7							
8							

	Observations
Antacid 1	
Antacid 2	
Antacid 3	
Antacid 4	

Protect Your Melon

Protective Head Gear

Time Required: 45-60 minutes for planning
and build; 30-35 minutes for testing

How this learning experience meets the
national science education standards:

Content Standard A: Science as Inquiry: As a result of activities in grades 5-8, all students should develop:

Abilities necessary to do scientific inquiry
- Identify questions that can be answered through scientific investigations.
- Design and conduct a scientific investigation.
- Use appropriate tools and techniques to gather, analyze and interpret data.
- Develop descriptions, explanations, predictions and models using evidence.
- Think critically and logically to make the relationships between evidence and explanations.
- Recognize and analyze alternative explanations and predictions.
- Communicate scientific procedures and explanations.
- Use mathematics in all aspects of scientific inquiry.

Understanding Scientific Inquiry
- Different kinds of questions suggest different kinds of scientific investigations.
- Current scientific knowledge and understanding guide scientific investigations.
- Mathematics is important in all aspects of scientific inquiry.
- Technology used to gather data enhances accuracy and allows scientists to analyze and quantify results of investigations.
- Scientific explanations emphasize evidence, have logically consistent arguments, and use scientific principles, models and theories.
- Science advances through legitimate skepticism.
- Scientific investigations sometimes result in new ideas and phenomena for study, generate new methods or procedures for an investigation, or develop new technologies to improve the collection of data.

Content Standard B: Physical Science: As a result of activities in grades 5-8, all students should develop an understanding of:

Motion and Forces
- An object that is not being subjected to a force will continue to move at a constant speed and in a straight line.

- If more than one force acts on an object along a straight line, then the forces will reinforce or cancel one another, depending on their direction and magnitude. Unbalanced forces will cause changes in the speed or direction of an object's motion.

Transfer of Energy
- Energy is a property of many substances and is associated with heat, light, electricity, mechanical motion, sound, nuclei, and the nature of a chemical. Energy is transferred in many ways.

Content Standard E: Science and Technology: As a result of activities in grades 5-8, all students should develop:
- Abilities of technological design
- Identify appropriate problems for technological design.
- Design a solution or a product.
- Implement a proposed design.
- Evaluate completed technological designs or products.
- Communicate the process of technological design.

Understanding about science and technology
- Scientific inquiry and technological design have similarities and differences. Scientists propose explanations for questions about the natural world, and engineers propose solutions relating to human problems, needs, and aspirations. Technological solutions are temporary; technologies exist within nature and so they cannot contravene physical or biological principles; technological solutions have side effects; and technologies cost, carry risks, and provide benefits.
- Science and technology are reciprocal. Science helps drive technology, as it addresses questions that demand more sophisticated instruments and provides principles for better instrumentation and technique. Technology is essential to science, because it provides instruments and techniques that enable observations of objects and phenomena that are otherwise unobservable due to factors such as quantity, distance, location, size, and speed. Technology also provides tools for investigations, inquiry, and analysis.
- Perfectly designed solutions do not exist. All technological solutions have trade-offs, such as safety, cost, efficiency, and appearance. Engineers often build in back-up systems to provide safety. Risk is part of living in a highly technological world. Reducing risk often results in new technology.
- Technological designs have constraints. Some constraints are unavoidable, for example, properties of materials, or effects of weather and friction; other constraints limit choices in the design, for example, environmental protection, human safety, and aesthetics.
- Technological solutions have intended benefits and unintended consequences. Some consequences can be predicted, others cannot.

CONTENT STANDARD G:
As a result of activities in grades 5-8, all students should develop understanding of:
Nature of Science
- Scientists formulate and test their explanations of nature using observation, experiments, and theoretical and mathematical models. Although all scientific ideas are tentative and subject to change and improvement in principle, for most major ideas in science, there is much experimental and observational confirmation. Those ideas are not likely to change greatly in the future. Scientists do and have changed their ideas about nature when they encounter new experimental evidence that does not match their existing explanations.

How this learning experience meets the National Standards for Technological Literacy:
- Standard 1. Students will develop an understanding of the characteristics and scope of technology.
- Standard 2. Students will develop an understanding of the core concepts of technology.
- Standard 4. Students will develop an understanding of the cultural, social, economic, and political effects of technology.

- Standard 8. Students will develop an understanding of the attributes of design.
- Standard 9. Students will develop an understanding of engineering design.
- Standard 10. Students will develop an understanding of the role of troubleshooting, research and development, invention and innovation, and experimentation in problem solving.
- Standard 13. Students will develop the abilities to assess the impact of products and systems.

Overview:

In this activity, students will learn about protecting their melon "head" from damage in a fall through a challenge to design a cost effective helmet. Students will design a helmet to protect a melon when it is dropped vertically. The winning design will be the one that best protects the melon at the lowest cost.

Background:

Protective helmets have become standard equipment in many sports and activities. Our bodies are designed so that the rigid skull protects the brain. But head injuries that involve a sudden collision between our heads and something hard can result in bruising and swelling of the brain. When the injured brain tissue swells up, it builds up pressure as it presses against the inside of the skull bones. This can result in further damage. Protective helmets are designed to cushion the head and minimize the impact of a collision.

Bicycle helmets are one type of protective head gear. The Consumer Product Safety Commission (CPSC) has developed manufacturing and testing standards for bicycle helmets. Helmets are tested to make sure that they do not:
- Block the rider's vision.
- Come off when the rider falls.
- Use straps that do not stretch enough to let it come off in an accident or fall, and
- To significantly reduce the force to the rider's head when it hits a hard surface.

The last standard is the focus of this activity.

Teacher Notes:

Cantaloupe or honeydew melons are recommended for this activity. However, large ripe tomatoes may also be used as the model for the helmet. Testing should be done outside, using a ladder or a stairwell with a clear path to the ground. Line the landing area with plastic tablecloths, a paint drop cloth or newspaper prior to testing. Since materials will vary depending on availability, a specific materials cost list must be prepared prior to the activity. See notes in "Getting Started" below.

Safety Notes:

1. Place the newspaper, tablecloth or drop cloth on the floor beneath the testing area.
2. Ensure that students stay far back from the testing area.
3. Only adults should conduct drop tests.
4. If using a ladder, have another adult hold the base of the ladder during the duration of the test.

Getting Started:

1. Define testing area and parameters for students. The "helmets" should be dropped on to a hard surface covered with plastic or newspaper. Do not drop on grassy or uneven surfaces.
2. Set up a 'store' with available materials, and price materials for students. Specify the cost per amount of material; for example, $.50 for a 6 inch x 6 inch square of plastic. Price the most desirable materials higher, such as tape or foam, to discourage extensive use of these materials. Consider limiting the amount of tape and other desirable materials to encourage innovation. Post the materials cost list on the board or in a handout.

3. Distribute purchase orders to student teams. Keep extra purchase orders for additional materials requests.
4. Review design parameters with students.

Materials needed per team of 3-4 students:

- Melon, cantaloupe or honeydew
- Sharpie or other permanent marker
- Purchase Order sheet
- Scissors
- Masking tape
- Variety of scrap materials such as: 3 straws, 2 paper plates, 2 balloons, cloth scraps, foil, newspaper, waxed paper, plastic wrap and any available recyclables.

Procedure:

1. Each team begins by drawing a face (eyes, nose and mouth) on one side of the melon. The helmet they design MUST allow the entire face to remain uncovered.

2. Explain the design challenge to the students: Weighing cost against performance, they must design a cost effective helmet to protect their melon 'head' from injury in a fall. They can use any combination of materials provided, but the winning design will be the one that protects the melon from cracking or breaking when dropped from the highest point at the lowest cost. The melons will be dropped from a vertical height beginning at 6.5 feet (2 meters) and increasing until all melons have cracked, or the teacher has dropped from as high as possible. Teams should record the highest successful drop, i.e. the height attained prior to cracking or breaking, and their final total cost of materials.

3. Allow students to view the materials choices, and ask questions about availability and cost. Explain that each team will plan its design, and develop a materials list and associated costs on their purchase order. Emphasize the need to plan carefully because, although they will be allowed to purchase additional materials after the initial order, those additional materials will cost two times the initial cost.

4. To acquire materials, teams must bring a completed purchase order (see student handout) including team member names; materials they wish to purchase and the amount of each they are requesting; the cost per unit of each material and the total cost. If additional materials are purchased after the initial order, a new purchase order must be completed, and a 100% materials cost surcharge will be added to the team total.

5. Allow students 45-60 minutes to complete building of the helmet design. Testing can be done immediately after the build, or in the next class period.

6. To test helmets, arrange students safely away from drop area. Beginning at a height of 6.5 feet (2 meters), drop (do not throw) each helmeted melon. If the melon cracks or breaks in the fall, the team is eliminated. Increase the height and continue testing until all melons have cracked or broken; or the maximum testing height has been reached.

7. Upon return to the classroom, collect the drop height and cost of each team's helmet. Remind students that the last successful drop height is the one prior to cracking or breaking, and also to include any materials surcharges in their total cost. Lead a discussion about cost vs. performance, materials selection, etc. Discussion questions (can also be used for written reflection) can include:

- How did the cost of your helmet relate to the success of the drop test? (Answers will vary, but the class may see some correlation between low cost and lower performance. With regard to bicycle helmets on the market, most helmets are designed to meet the specifications of the CPSC standard for performance. Basic designs are often consistent between lower and higher priced helmets. The differences often lie in the quality and quantity of materials, such as using lower density foam padding or smaller air vents.)

- What was the most (least) useful material you used? Why? (some students may comment on the cushion or shock absorption properties of the foam or packing materials; others may have thought some materials would be helpful but they were not in the end)

- What would you do differently if given the chance? (answers will vary)

- How did you protect your melon's 'face' for the drop? (Answers will vary; look for a correlation between the cost of the helmet and facial protection results)

- How did factoring in cost affect your design? (Answers will vary)

- Did a melon work well as a substitute for a human head? Why or why not? (A melon is a reasonable substitute for a human head because it, like the head, has a more rigid outside and a softer inside, is fragile and can be broken or damaged. The human skull might survive a higher drop without cracking, but the brain inside will likely be significantly damaged from moving around inside the skull.)

- Where do you think the energy from the melon dropping went when it hit the ground? (If the melon did not break or crack, the materials used in the helmet absorbed enough of the impact energy to protect it. If not, the melon absorbed the energy.)

Head Gear
Student Sheet

Purchase Order Number _____
(if higher than 1, apply 100% cost surcharge below)

Team members: _____

Material Requested	Quantity or Amount	Unit Cost ($ per ____)	Total Cost
Total Materials Cost			$
With Materials Surcharge for orders 2 and higher (total cost x 2)			$

Purchase Order Number _____
(if higher than 1, apply 100% cost surcharge below)

Team members: _____

Material Requested	Quantity or Amount	Unit Cost ($ per ____)	Total Cost
Total Materials Cost			$
With Materials Surcharge for orders 2 and higher (total cost x 2)			$

Biomedical Engineering Crossword Puzzle

Across

3. Chemotherapy drugs are often administered directly into a vein through an intravenous _____.

6. Protective helmets have become standard equipment in many _____ and activities.

8. Protective helmets are designed to cushion the head and _____ the impact of a collision.

11. Biomedical engineering with an _____ emphasis is a popular choice among students.

12. _____ engineering or biomechanics is the specialty that sees the human body as a mechanical structure.

14. Assistive _____ includes devices such as powered wheelchairs, talking computers, and hearing aids.

15. Our body's circulatory system is comprised of three parts: pulmonary, coronary, and _____.

16. Esophagus muscles are smooth or _____.

17. The objective of biomedical engineering is to enhance health care by solving complex _____ problems using engineering principles.

18. Bioelectrical engineers are often responsible for developing machines that are used to _____ and treat disease.

19. Biochemical engineers concern themselves with body responses on a _____ level.

Down

1. The esophagus uses _____ to move food toward the stomach.

2. _____ pain can be as simple as indigestion or gas buildup to more serious conditions such as ulcers or chronic acid reflux.

4. Clinical engineers may also evaluate equipment prior to purchase, test the equipment for safety, or _____ existing hospital equipment.

5. Rehabilitation engineers participate in the research and development of technology to assist people with _____.

7. BMETs must be quick _____.

9. A wave of muscle contraction that pushes food down into stomach.

10. Humans have about 206 bones that make up body shape and protect internal _____.

13. Biomedical engineers may design systems to _____ the human body while snowboarding to aid in injury prevention.

Biomedical Engineering Crossword Puzzle

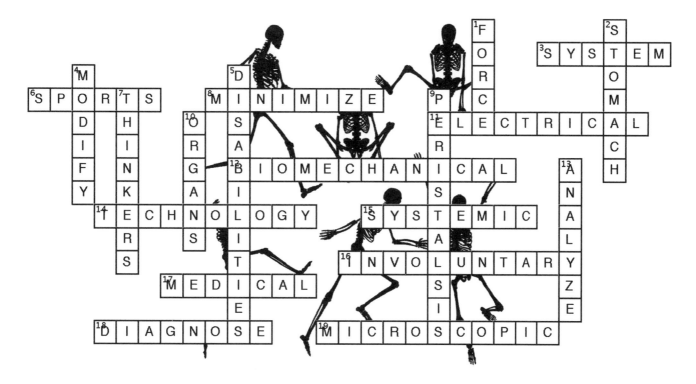

Across

3. Chemotherapy drugs are often administered directly into a vein through an intravenous _____. [system]
6. Protective helmets have become standard equipment in many _____ and activities. [sports]
8. Protective helmets are designed to cushion the head and _____ the impact of a collision. [minimize]
11. Biomedical engineering with an _____ emphasis is a popular choice among students. [electrical]
12. _____ engineering or biomechanics is the specialty that sees the human body as a mechanical structure. [Biomechanical]
14. Assistive _____ includes devices such as powered wheelchairs, talking computers, and hearing aids. [technology]
15. Our body's circulatory system is comprised of three parts: pulmonary, coronary, and _____. [systemic]
16. Esophagus muscles are smooth or _____. [involuntary]
17. The objective of biomedical engineering is to enhance health care by solving complex _____ problems using engineering principles. [medical]
18. Bioelectrical engineers are often responsible for developing machines that are used to _____ and treat disease. [diagnose]

Down

1. The esophagus uses _____ to move food toward the stomach. [force]
2. _____ pain can be as simple as indigestion or gas buildup to more serious conditions such as ulcers or chronic acid reflux. [stomach]
4. Clinical engineers may also evaluate equipment prior to purchase, test the equipment for safety, or _____ existing hospital equipment. [modify]
5. Rehabilitation engineers participate in the research and development of technology to assist people with _____. [disabilities]
7. BMETs must be quick _____. [thinkers]
9. A wave of muscle contraction that pushes food down into stomach. [Peristalsis]
10. Humans have about 206 bones that make up body shape and protect internal _____. [organs]
13. Biomedical engineers may design systems to _____ the human body while snowboarding to aid in injury prevention. [analyze]

Biomedical Engineering
Wordseach Puzzle

```
L  I  I  W  Z  N  K  K  F  D  B  O  G  F  H  A  T  K  R  V  S  I  S  Z  C
C  H  C  A  M  O  T  S  E  J  X  W  V  J  M  E  M  A  H  R  G  N  G  V  O
Z  T  E  C  H  N  O  L  O  G  Y  Z  I  X  D  F  E  J  U  Z  A  M  B  K  H
M  T  L  F  M  E  T  S  Y  S  B  B  N  O  I  C  D  A  Y  G  T  P  V  F  W
D  G  S  X  C  P  T  L  W  K  I  K  V  J  A  S  I  O  R  F  S  K  Y  K  G
G  P  X  K  I  J  N  K  Q  M  O  V  O  T  G  Y  C  O  A  R  I  P  Z  I  V
M  W  S  O  P  U  I  H  K  U  M  Y  L  P  N  U  A  N  E  J  M  D  W  I  P
Y  J  I  W  O  U  M  A  W  J  E  E  U  I  O  R  L  K  I  M  P  F  O  Q  T
J  Z  S  N  C  R  P  N  T  L  C  D  N  P  S  B  N  A  X  I  Z  G  Y  M  M
Y  F  L  P  S  Y  F  A  E  C  H  L  T  S  E  I  R  O  T  N  Q  B  J  C  P
E  E  A  L  O  S  Q  L  S  N  A  V  A  Y  H  T  E  P  U  I  S  T  O  N  D
J  W  T  N  R  T  D  Y  R  X  N  M  R  T  Q  I  A  Q  O  M  V  G  T  R  H
J  Q  S  V  C  R  G  Z  I  N  I  H  Y  E  K  J  N  Q  P  I  C  I  N  U  Y
P  U  I  A  I  O  H  E  P  V  C  J  H  T  P  U  T  E  X  Z  S  N  M  P  I
U  I  R  H  M  P  R  T  A  Y  A  J  Y  H  N  C  B  F  G  E  A  F  T  A  S
F  M  E  O  V  S  H  D  L  C  L  E  K  M  F  S  X  T  M  H  X  C  T  M  D
S  Q  P  M  O  G  E  D  I  S  A  B  I  L  I  T  I  E  S  I  L  P  W  R  Q
```

1. Rehabilitation engineers participate in the research and development of technology to assist people with _____.

2. _____ engineering or biomechanics is the specialty that sees the human body as a mechanical structure.

3. A wave of muscle contraction that pushes food down into stomach.

4. Biochemical engineers concern themselves with body responses on a _____ level.

5. Protective helmets are designed to cushion the head and _____ the impact of a collision.

6. Esophagus muscles are smooth or _____.

7. Bioelectrical engineers are often responsible for developing machines that are used to _____ and treat disease.

8. Assistive _____ includes devices such as powered wheelchairs, talking computers, and hearing aids.

9. BMETs must be quick _____.

10. The objective of biomedical engineering is to enhance health care by solving complex _____ problems using engineering principles.

11. _____ pain can be as simple as indigestion to more serious conditions such as ulcers or chronic acid reflux.

12. Chemotherapy drugs are often administered directly into a vein through an intravenous _____.

13. Humans have about 206 bones that make up body shape and protect internal _____.

14. Protective helmets have become standard equipment in many _____.

15. Biomedical engineers may design systems to _____ the human body while snowboarding to aid in injury prevention.

16. Clinical engineers may evaluate equipment prior to purchase, test the equipment for safety, or _____ existing hospital equipment.

Biomedical Engineering
Wordseach Puzzle

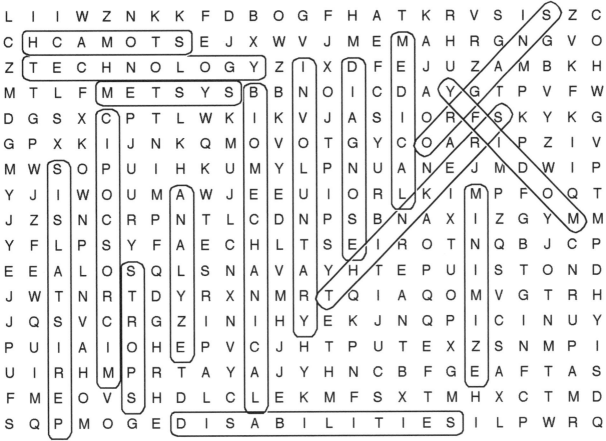

```
L  I  I  W  Z  N  K  K  F  D  B  O  G  F  H  A  T  K  R  V  S  I  S  Z  C
C  H  C  A  M  O  T  S  E  J  X  W  V  J  M  E  M  A  H  R  G  N  G  V  O
Z  T  E  C  H  N  O  L  O  G  Y  Z  I  X  D  F  E  J  U  Z  A  M  B  K  H
M  T  L  F  M  E  T  S  Y  S  B  B  N  O  I  C  D  A  Y  G  T  P  V  F  W
D  G  S  X  C  P  T  L  W  K  I  K  V  J  A  S  I  O  R  F  S  K  Y  K  G
G  P  X  K  I  J  N  K  Q  M  O  V  O  T  G  Y  C  O  A  R  I  P  Z  I  V
M  W  S  O  P  U  I  H  K  U  M  Y  L  P  N  U  A  N  E  J  M  D  W  I  P
Y  J  I  W  O  U  M  A  W  J  E  E  U  I  O  R  L  K  I  M  P  F  O  Q  T
J  Z  S  N  C  R  P  N  T  L  C  D  N  P  S  B  N  A  X  I  Z  G  Y  M  M
Y  F  L  P  S  Y  F  A  E  C  H  L  T  S  E  I  R  O  T  N  Q  B  J  C  P
E  E  A  L  O  S  Q  L  S  N  A  V  A  Y  H  T  E  P  U  I  S  T  O  N  D
J  W  T  N  R  T  D  Y  R  X  N  M  R  T  Q  I  A  Q  O  M  V  G  T  R  H
J  Q  S  V  C  R  G  Z  I  N  I  H  Y  E  K  J  N  Q  P  I  C  I  N  U  Y
P  U  I  A  I  O  H  E  P  V  C  J  H  T  P  U  T  E  X  Z  S  N  M  P  I
U  I  R  H  M  P  R  T  A  Y  A  J  Y  H  N  C  B  F  G  E  A  F  T  A  S
F  M  E  O  V  S  H  D  L  C  L  E  K  M  F  S  X  T  M  H  X  C  T  M  D
S  Q  P  M  O  G  E  D  I  S  A  B  I  L  I  T  I  E  S  I  L  P  W  R  Q
```

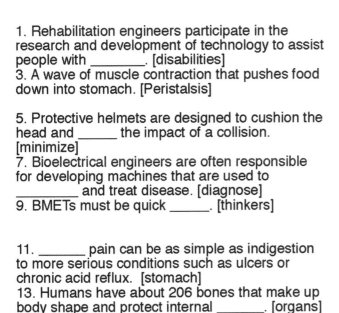

1. Rehabilitation engineers participate in the research and development of technology to assist people with _____. [disabilities]

3. A wave of muscle contraction that pushes food down into stomach. [Peristalsis]

5. Protective helmets are designed to cushion the head and _____ the impact of a collision. [minimize]

7. Bioelectrical engineers are often responsible for developing machines that are used to _____ and treat disease. [diagnose]

9. BMETs must be quick _____. [thinkers]

11. _____ pain can be as simple as indigestion to more serious conditions such as ulcers or chronic acid reflux. [stomach]

13. Humans have about 206 bones that make up body shape and protect internal _____. [organs]

15. Biomedical engineers may design systems to _____ the human body while snowboarding to aid in injury prevention. [analyze]

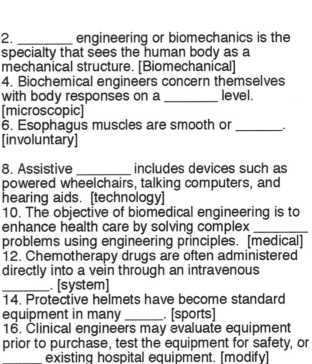

2. _____ engineering or biomechanics is the specialty that sees the human body as a mechanical structure. [Biomechanical]

4. Biochemical engineers concern themselves with body responses on a _____ level. [microscopic]

6. Esophagus muscles are smooth or _____. [involuntary]

8. Assistive _____ includes devices such as powered wheelchairs, talking computers, and hearing aids. [technology]

10. The objective of biomedical engineering is to enhance health care by solving complex _____ problems using engineering principles. [medical]

12. Chemotherapy drugs are often administered directly into a vein through an intravenous _____. [system]

14. Protective helmets have become standard equipment in many _____. [sports]

16. Clinical engineers may evaluate equipment prior to purchase, test the equipment for safety, or _____ existing hospital equipment. [modify]

Electrical Engineering

Electrical Engineering

The diverse and progressive fields of electrical and electronic engineering have grown rapidly and employ 725,000 engineers, making it the largest branch of engineering. Electrical engineers are imaginative problem solvers who enjoy challenges.

According to the Institute of Electrical and Electronic Engineering, "Electrical engineering is about 100 years old, and electronics has been a science for only about 75 years. Electrical engineers (EEs) specializing in power work with motors and generators; and design transmission lines and power plants. EEs specializing in electronics deal with communications, such as radio, television, and telephony; and with digital and analog circuit technologies. All engineers draw from the fundamentals of science and mathematics. They design and work with electrical, electronic, electro-optical, and electromechanical devices, circuits, and systems.

They collaborate with other professionals in developing sophisticated software tools that support design, verification, and testing. Electrical engineering is a discipline that integrates many other disciplines, such as physics, chemistry, mathematics, computer software and hardware, solid-state electronics, communications, electromagnetics and optics, signals and signal processing, systems science, reliability, engineering economics, and manufacturing."

The developments of electrical and electronic engineers are everywhere. There are thousands of electrical devices and systems available today that electrical engineers have somehow touched. Anything you plug into the wall – stereos, computers, microwaves, televisions, power tools, air conditioners, and major appliances – has somehow involved an electrical engineer. Even things you can't plug into the wall – satellites, cellular phones, and beepers – have been designed, manufactured, or modified by electrical engineers.

Major specializations within electrical engineering include power plant/energy, communications, optical engineering, and computer engineering. Electrical engineers who specialize in power applications may work for utility companies designing power distribution systems; or they may work on generating electricity by using alternative energy sources.

Communications is also a large field within electrical engineering. Just think about the amazing information superhighway (Internet). Millions of people connect simultaneously to the vast network of information. At home, people use the Internet for entertainment, shopping, and to enhance their hobbies and activities. Communications specialists also try to improve radio signals, television, and telephone connections. As a communications specialist, you may design a very fast and affordable videophone

om Westenburg, Principal Engineer,
nited States Olympic Committee

"I became involved in sports engineering in a roundabout way. I was always interested in sports growing up, but didn't realize that I could make a career out of it. I was a distance runner in college, and also did low-level racing in sailing and skiing. Growing up I liked to figure out how things worked. I as good at math and science and, as a teenager, ecame interested in music, stereos, and sound rocessing. I was interested in many different elds of study, but electronics was the area that ally grabbed my attention.

My father was an engineer at Lawrence ivermore Lab but never really talked about here he worked. One time he managed to get pproval to take me on a tour of the facility. couldn't believe there was so much cool quipment! It was fascinating and mind-boggling. rom that point on I was hooked. I had to go into ngineering.

My first job as an electrical engineer was with hillips Corporation in Holland, working on ntegrated circuit designs. I was lucky and able o work in an area that did instrumentation; and ome interesting music and audio applications, uch as Dolby TM noise reduction and some f the early work in digital audio and voice ynthesis. My main focus was to convert nalog signals into digital values for real-time rocessing or storage. At this point I had no idea hat this same technology would lead me into pace applications, and eventually into sports ngineering. For example, instrumentation is eeded to monitor the speed of your car, the osition of the space shuttle, or the impact force f a boxers punch.

I had previously toured the Olympic Training enter and thought it would be the ideal job to vork at developing state-of-the-art equipment o enhance an athlete's performance. Years later I came through Colorado on a ski trip and noticed the engineering center's position in the newspaper. I applied immediately and have been with the U.S. Olympic Committee ever since. I design various electronic devices to measure athletic performance. These are custom, sports-specific systems that aren't commercially available. The instrumentation can look at impact forces, monitor position, or whatever the sport needs to try and help an athlete improve. It's a lot of data acquisition, sensor, and embedded controller design. One thing that I love is that it's always changing, and I never know what my next project will involve.

"A few years ago we did a project for swimming that was very successful. The idea came from a coach who thought that if a swimmer could learn what it felt like to swim faster, with assistance, then, when the assistance was removed the athlete would be able to progress quicker (plus he saw something like this in Moscow).

We started looking at this and came up with basically a miniature ski lift over the pool. It had a cable about nine feet above the water that attached to a tether, and a harness around the athlete's waist. It used steel cable, and needed about 4,000 pounds of tension in it. This required wall anchors, guy wires, guide pulleys, etc. At that point, I'm glad we took a step back and realized that the high tension was really just to keep the weight of the cable from sagging.

"We changed to a small Vectran cable (10 times the strength of steel by weight) and only needed about 300 pounds of tension, which allowed us to do away with almost all of the extraneous hardware. This new version was very simple and not nearly as impressive looking as the indoor ski lift would have been, but it allowed us to just mount the system into standard pool starting block holes.

"The next issue was how to drive the cable to tow the athlete. Having a high-power electric motor on a pool deck didn't seem very safe. So we went with a hydraulic motor. Then we moved the drive motor and a hydraulic pump down to the pool pump area. This kept the noise away from the athletes and coaches, as well as the high voltage.

"Then we looked at types of hydraulic fluid, in case a line broke and fluid was spilled into the pool with athletes in it. Some types are fairly toxic, so we went with a fluid about like vegetable oil. Unfortunately, this went rancid after a few months, since anything could grow in it. Later we went with a very safe but just slightly toxic fluid. A person needs to drink over a liter before it would cause problems, so if an athlete drank some from a film in the pool, it would be totally safe.

"Everybody in the first group to use this system set personal records at their first competition, and two set world records. This was after only six weeks of training, so we felt like the system did work, and the concept was solid. In my position at the U.S. Olympic Committee I get to work with some of the best athletes in the world, and get to experience many sports that I never knew existed until I took this job. Many times the designers are also the "test pilots," so we get to try out a new instrumented boxing bag, take a luge sled down a start ramp, or paddle our instrumented kayak.

Like I said before, I never know what to expect next, but I wouldn't want it any other way."

According to The Institute of Electrical and Electronic Engineering (IEEE), "The key to employability is acquiring the knowledge and skill sets in demand by employers. Those who fail to gain or maintain knowledge and skill with tools, such as computer-aided design (CAD) and other software relevant to their work, are disadvantaged. The lack of communication and interpersonal skills needed to work effectively on teams, can also be a stumbling block."

IEEE has a fantastic Web site at www.ieee.org that is jam-packed with information about the world of electrical engineering. See the numerous branches within the world's largest technical professional society. The Web site has pages on internships and scholarships. It lists information on job hunting and has a job bank. Twenty-five percent of the world's technical papers are produced each year through the IEEE. The institute has student chapters at numerous universities, and offers student benefits such as group insurance programs, credit cards, auto and education loans, copy service discounts, and car rental discounts. Students receive the IEEE SPECTRUM magazine and a discount on membership. The Web site is well worth the time invested in browsing it.

Electronic/Electrical Engineering Technology

Electronic engineering technologists design, develop, and manufacture everything that you plug into the wall - televisions, computers, refrigerators, microwaves, stereos, etc. They design, develop, work on and work with the electronic components that are in every device that runs on electricity. They are into electronic equipment, such as communication equipment; radar, industrial wireless and medical monitoring or control devices; navigational equipment; and computers. They also manage and support cars that today have many electronic components: GPS, phones, Internet, electronic devices that allow the car to park without the intervention of the driver and the navigational systems that allow you to verbally tell the car to go to a specific place and the car will drive for you.

lectrical engineering technologists apply their skills
the generation and transmission of electricity.
any electrical engineering technologists work in
een energy for solar panel, wind turbine, wave
ergy and geothermal design companies.

Electronic engineering technicians repair
id maintaining electronic equipment used by
isinesses or individuals. They may work in product
aluation and testing, using measuring and

agnostic devices such as oscilloscopes, computer
iftware and multimeters to adjust, test, and repair
juipment.

Electronics have revolutionized the world.
verything from iPods, to cell phones, to GPS systems
intain electronic components. Every business
om the small shop owner, to utility companies, to
deral government agencies, need technologists and
chnicians. The opportunities are far-reaching and
undant. So often, the engineering technologist or
chnician can save the day by helping companies
in smoother and more efficiently.

- The small shop owner and large companies
  may not have a technician on staff, but
  when a machine breaks down, they call a
  field technician to fix the problem. The field
  technician may be responsible for installing
  and ensuring the normal operation of
  machines located within several companies
  in a certain geographic area. When
  equipment breaks down, the technician will
  first check for common causes of trouble,
  such as loose connections or obviously
  defective components. If routine checks do
  not locate the trouble, the technician may
  refer to schematics or repair manuals that

show connections and provide instructions
on how to locate problems. Many
technicians will use software programs,
multimeters, oscilloscopes, spectrum
analyzers and signal generators in their
diagnoses. If a machine cannot be repaired
on-site, the field technician will arrange to
transport the machine to a facility or repair
shop where a bench technician can repair
it. Some equipment may give an alarm
if failing and other equipment may just
break. The technician will likely be working
on equipment from different technological
era's.

- Alternative energy companies may
  hire technologists to design, develop or
  manufacture equipment for wind turbines
  and farms, solar panels and car recharging
  stations, or equipment to harvest and
  transmit energy from dams or other sources
  of electricity.
- Utility companies will hire engineering
  technologist as plant or electrical system
  operators. They most often hire technicians
  to do everything from installing, operating,
  maintaining, and controlling electric
  substations, to monitoring equipment
  and electric transformers that distribute
  electricity to homes and businesses.
- Federal government agencies hire
  technologists and technicians to maintain
  national security equipment, air traffic
  control systems, U.S. postal facilities,
  equipment in customs offices, the U.S. Mint,
  the Federal Reserve, the White House, and
  NASA space centers.

Optical Engineering

Optical engineering is a progressive and exciting field. Optical engineers design and develop devices and measurement systems, such as lasers and fiber optics that utilize the properties of light.

Lasers are used in many different kinds of applications. Medical doctors use lasers to cut out birthmarks and cancerous growths. They fix detached retinas, cauterize wounds, and vaporize kidney stones. Your home and car CD players use laser light to play your favorite music. Laser printers and supermarket scanners are other examples of how laser technology has merged into our lives.

Fiber optics is another expanding branch of optical engineering. Fiber optics are hair-sized strands of glass that carry voice and video information over long distances in pulses of light. Fiber optic systems run all over the world. They run across the country and even underwater to neighboring countries.

Optical engineers of the future may design new virtual reality games or air combat simulators. They may seek to optimize CD storage capacity or develop new medical applications, such as those in telemedicine. They may focus on making the Internet faster and even more accessible.

The International Society for Optical Engineering (SPIE) has a great Web site at www.spie.org that is packed with information about the world of optical engineering as well as contests, videos and scholarships.

Bright Light
Batteries, Bulbs and Light

Time Required: 45-60 minutes

Content Standard A: Science as Inquiry: As a result of activities in grades 5-8, all students should develop:
Abilities necessary to do scientific inquiry
- Identify questions that can be answered through scientific investigations.
- Design and conduct a scientific investigation.
- Use appropriate tools and techniques to gather, analyze and interpret data.
- Develop descriptions, explanations, predictions and models using evidence.
- Think critically and logically to make the relationships between evidence and explanations.
- Recognize and analyze alternative explanations and predictions.
- Communicate scientific procedures and explanations.
- Use mathematics in all aspects of scientific inquiry.

Understanding Scientific Inquiry
- Different kinds of questions suggest different kinds of scientific investigations.
- Current scientific knowledge and understanding guide scientific investigations.
- Mathematics is important in all aspects of scientific inquiry.
- Technology used to gather data enhances accuracy and allows scientists to analyze and quantify results of investigations.
- Scientific explanations emphasize evidence, have logically consistent arguments, and use scientific principles, models and theories.
- Science advances through legitimate skepticism.
- Scientific investigations sometimes result in new ideas and phenomena for study, generate new methods or procedures for an investigation, or develop new technologies to improve the collection of data.

Content Standard B: As a result of their activities in grades 5-8, all students should develop an understanding of:
Transfer of Energy
- Energy is a property of many substances and is associated with heat, light, electricity, mechanical motion, sound, nuclei, and the nature of a chemical. Energy is transferred in many ways.
- Light interacts with matter by transmission (including refraction), absorption, or scattering (including reflection). To see an object, light from that object--emitted by or scattered from it--must enter the eye.
- Electrical circuits provide a means of transferring electrical energy when heat, light, sound, and

chemical changes are produced.
- In most chemical and nuclear reactions, energy is transferred into or out of a system. Heat, light, mechanical motion, or electricity might all be involved in such transfers.

Content Standard E: Science and Technology: As a result of activities in grades 5-8, al students should develop:

Abilities of technological design
- Identify appropriate problems for technological design.
- Design a solution or a product.
- Implement a proposed design.
- Evaluate completed technological designs or products.
- Communicate the process of technological design.

Understanding about science and technology
- Scientific inquiry and technological design have similarities and differences. Scientists propose explanations for questions about the natural world, and engineers propose solutions relating to human problems, needs, and aspirations. Technological solutions are temporary; technologies exist within nature and so they cannot contravene physical or biological principles; technological solutions have side effects; and technologies cost, carry risks, and provide benefits.
- Science and technology are reciprocal. Science helps drive technology, as it addresses questions that demand more sophisticated instruments and provides principles for better instrumentation and technique. Technology is essential to science, because it provides instruments and techniques that enable observations of objects and phenomena that are otherwise unobservable due to factors such as quantity, distance, location, size, and speed. Technology also provides tools for investigations, inquiry, and analysis.
- Perfectly designed solutions do not exist. All technological solutions have trade-offs, such as safety, cost efficiency, and appearance. Engineers often build in back-up systems to provide safety. Risk is part of living in a highly technological world. Reducing risk often results in new technology.
- Technological designs have constraints. Some constraints are unavoidable, for example, properties of materials, or effects of weather and friction; other constraints limit choices in the design, for example, environmental protection, human safety, and aesthetics.
- Technological solutions have intended benefits and unintended consequences. Some consequences can be predicted, others cannot.

How this learning experience meets the National Standards for Technological Literacy:
- Standard 1. Students will develop an understanding of the characteristics and scope of technology.
- Standard 2. Students will develop an understanding of the core concepts of technology.
- Standard 3. Students will develop an understanding of the relationships among technologies and the connections between technology and other fields of study.
- Standard 4. Students will develop an understanding of the cultural, social, economic, and political effects of technology
- Standard 5. Students will develop an understanding of the effects of technology on the environment.
- Standard 6. Students will develop an understanding of the role of society in the development and use of technology.
- Standard 8. Students will develop an understanding of the attributes of design.
- Standard 9. Students will develop an understanding of engineering design.
- Standard 10. Students will develop an understanding of the role of troubleshooting, research and development, invention and innovation, and experimentation in problem solving.

Overview:

Using a simple circuit and LED (light emitting diode) bulbs, students will build a flashlight.

Background:

Flashlights are portable light sources convenient for us to carry around. They have a common general structure regardless of the type of bulb used: A tube to hold the parts together; a bulb, a reflective surface and a simple battery circuit. Many flashlights, particularly older ones, use an incandescent or tungsten filament bulb. Tungsten is the metal that makes up the wire completing the battery powered circuit. When electricity flows through the metal, it heats up and glows, creating visible light. The shiny material near the bulb reflects the light.

LED flashlights use a different kind of bulb called a light emitting diode. LEDs are tiny lights that fit well in an electrical circuit. The light they emit is produced as a result of electrons moving in a special material called a semiconductor. Semiconductors are materials that conduct electricity at some level. Semiconductors are made of a mix of materials; some conduct better than others depending on the mix of elements, and the ability each has to move electricity.

LEDs have some advantages over incandescent bulbs. First, they don't have a metal wire or filament that will burn out. They are more durable, since they are covered in plastic instead of glass. And most importantly, they are very efficient. Incandescent bulbs must get very hot, to produce light. LED light is created when electricity makes the electrons of the material move, so most of the incoming energy is used to light the bulb instead of heating it.

Before building a flashlight, it's a good idea to draw schematics. Drawing schematics is essential for understanding electronic circuitry. Usually, in industry, engineers will draw a schematic of their design so that other people can understand how it works. A technician may use the schematic to test the circuit's conductivity. By building the design on a computer, the manufacturer can tell if it has any design errors. If no errors are found, manufacturing of the Printed Circuit Board (PCB) can begin.

A resistor is a device that resists the flow of electricity and is needed in this exercise so the LED does not burn out.

The symbol for a resistor in a schematic is:

The symbol for an LED in a schematic is:

The symbol for a battery is:

The flashlight the students will construct will consist of a simple circuit including a battery pack, batteries, wire, a resistor and an LED bulb, all enclosed in a tube made of recycled materials.

Teacher Notes:

1. You may use either coated wire (with ends stripped) or wire assemblies with alligator clips on the end.
2. Prepare materials in advance by stripping ends of wire (if not using alligator clips and wire).

Safety Notes:

Safety glasses should be used when testing the circuit.

Getting Started:

Prepare materials in advance for each team. Assemble in plastic baggie for easy distribution.

Materials needed per team of 3-4 students:

- 1 LED (color does not matter)
- 3 six inch long pieces of wire, either coated with ½ inch stripped on each end, or wire/alligator clip assemblies
- Electrical Tape
- 2 AA Batteries
- Battery holder
- Resistor
- Scrap materials to build housing: cardboard (cereal box weight), foam, aluminum foil, toilet paper or paper towel tubes, masking tape, plastic coffee stirrers, straws, etc)

Procedure:

Build the circuit below, using electrical tape or the alligator clips on wire ends to connect the components. The flow of electricity to and from the battery and LED is directional, so if the LED does not light, switch the direction of it with respect to the battery.

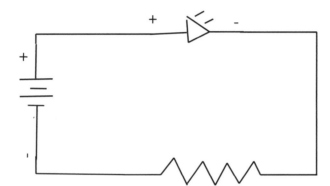

Once your circuit is working, design a container with the following constraints:

- Must contain all parts of the flashlight.
- Must reflect the light being produced.
- Must have a way to turn light off and on.
- Must be designed to be carried by one person.

After all teams have built their flashlights, ask each to present their design to the class.

Bright Light
Student Sheet

Did your circuit work the first time you turned it on? If not, why not? How did you correct the problem?

If you were to instruct someone else on how to build this circuit, what would you tell them to watch out for and why?

Carefully examine each experimental design set up shown below. Based on your experience with batteries and bulbs, circle each diagram that represents a successful method for lighting the bulb.

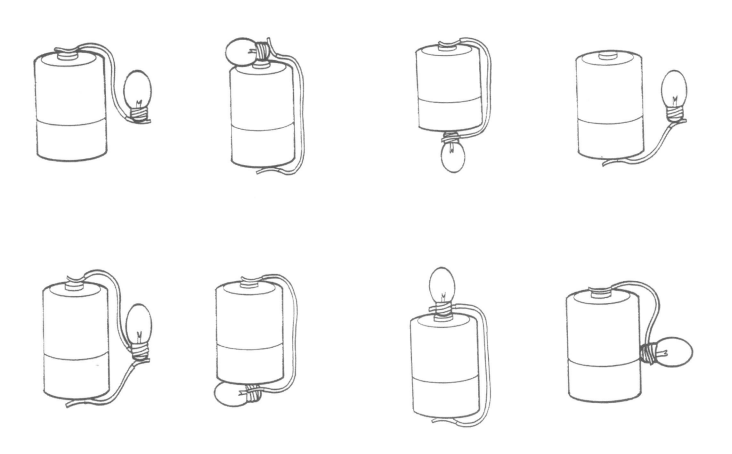

Bright Light
Answer Sheet

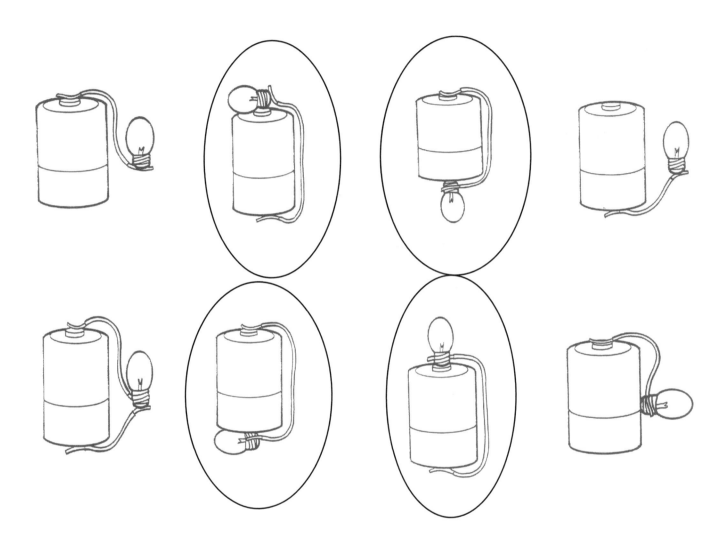

Putting it to the Test

Seeing the cause and effect

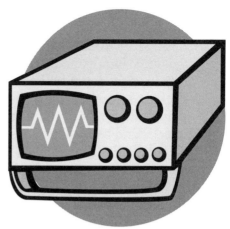

Time Required: 45-60 minutes

How this learning experience meets the national science education standards:

Content Standard A: Science as Inquiry: As a result of activities in grades 5-8, all students should develop:

Abilities necessary to do scientific inquiry
- Identify questions that can be answered through scientific investigations.
- Design and conduct a scientific investigation.
- Use appropriate tools and techniques to gather, analyze and interpret data.
- Develop descriptions, explanations, predictions and models using evidence.
- Think critically and logically to make the relationships between evidence and explanations.
- Recognize and analyze alternative explanations and predictions.
- Communicate scientific procedures and explanations.
- Use mathematics in all aspects of scientific inquiry.

Understanding Scientific Inquiry
- Different kinds of questions suggest different kinds of scientific investigations.
- Current scientific knowledge and understanding guide scientific investigations.
- Mathematics is important in all aspects of scientific inquiry.
- Technology used to gather data enhances accuracy and allows scientists to analyze and quantify results of investigations.
- Scientific explanations emphasize evidence, have logically consistent arguments, and use scientific principles, models and theories.
- Science advances through legitimate skepticism.
- Scientific investigations sometimes result in new ideas and phenomena for study, generate new methods or procedures for an investigation, or develop new technologies to improve the collection of data.

Content Standard B: As a result of their activities in grades 5-8, all students should develop an understanding of:

Transfer of Energy
- Energy is a property of many substances and is associated with heat, light, electricity, mechanical motion, sound, nuclei, and the nature of a chemical. Energy is transferred in many ways.
- Light interacts with matter by transmission (including refraction), absorption, or scattering (including reflection). To see an object, light from that object--emitted by or scattered from it--must enter the eye.
- Electrical circuits provide a means of transferring electrical energy when heat, light, sound, and chemical changes are produced.

- In most chemical and nuclear reactions, energy is transferred into or out of a system. Heat, light, mechanical motion, or electricity might all be involved in such transfers.

Content Standard E: Science and Technology: As a result of activities in grades 5-8, all students should develop:

Understanding about science and technology

- Scientific inquiry and technological design have similarities and differences. Scientists propose explanations for questions about the natural world, and engineers propose solutions relating to human problems, needs, and aspirations. Technological solutions are temporary; technologies exist within nature and so they cannot contravene physical or biological principles; technological solutions have side effects; and technologies cost, carry risks, and provide benefits.
- Science and technology are reciprocal. Science helps drive technology, as it addresses questions that demand more sophisticated instruments and provides principles for better instrumentation and technique. Technology is essential to science, because it provides instruments and techniques that enable observations of objects and phenomena that are otherwise unobservable due to factors such as quantity, distance, location, size, and speed. Technology also provides tools for investigations, inquiry, and analysis.
- Perfectly designed solutions do not exist. All technological solutions have trade-offs, such as safety, cost efficiency, and appearance. Engineers often build in back-up systems to provide safety. Risk is part of living in a highly technological world. Reducing risk often results in new technology.
- Technological designs have constraints. Some constraints are unavoidable, for example, properties of materials, or effects of weather and friction; other constraints limit choices in the design, for example, environmental protection, human safety, and aesthetics.
- Technological solutions have intended benefits and unintended consequences. Some consequences can be predicted, others cannot.

How this learning experience meets the National Standards for Technological Literacy:

- Standard 1. Students will develop an understanding of the characteristics and scope of technology.
- Standard 2. Students will develop an understanding of the core concepts of technology.
- Standard 3. Students will develop an understanding of the relationships among technologies and the connections between technology and other fields of study.
- Standard 10. Students will develop an understanding of the role of troubleshooting, research and development, invention and innovation, and experimentation in problem solving.

Overview:

Students will determine which materials conduct electricity.

Background:

- Conductors are materials which allow electrical current to flow through a material.
- Insulators are materials which stop the flow of electrical current.

Teacher Notes:

Any number of items can be substituted for the suggested list at the beginning of the learning experience. You just want to be certain that you have approximately equal numbers of conductors and insulators. Also be aware that you do not want to introduce the terms "insulator" or "conductor" until the students have engaged in the exploration, and have concrete experiences to connect to the terms. Students should be able to internalize the idea that conductors are materials that let electricity or electrical current pass through easily, while insulators are materials that do not allow electricity or electrical current to pass through easily.

Safety Notes:

Students should be told to keep wires away from all electrical outlets. If students create a short circuit, the wires will become hot. Students should disconnect the batteries. Monitor students as they move around the room testing different items and materials; make sure there is adequate space for students to move in and review safe handling of possible hazards in the area.

Getting Started:

1. Prepare bags of materials for each pair/group of students that contain the following:

   - Battery
   - Battery holder
   - 3 lead clips
   - Bulb
   - Bulb holder
   - Small piece of paper
   - A single key
   - Fork
   - Coin
   - Small piece of cloth
   - Plastic
   - Rock or stone
   - Eraser
   - Cork
   - Wood

2. Copy student sheets.

3. Be prepared to demonstrate how to successfully use the battery, battery holder, lead clips, bulb, and bulb holder, if necessary.

Materials Needed Per Pair of Students:

- Supply bags (as noted above)
- Student sheets

Procedure:

1. Assemble students into cooperative groups; designate pairs of students within the cooperative groups.
2. Present each pair of students with a supply bag; instruct students to remove the battery, battery holder, bulb, bulb holder, and lead clips.
3. Have the students make a circuit with the items removed, leaving only the ends of the wires free.
4. Challenge the students to test each of the remaining items in the bag by touching the material to be tested with both wires; observe to see if the bulb will light.
5. Sort the materials into two groups based on whether they helped the bulb light nor not.
6. Distribute student sheets; have the students record, in the appropriate space on the sheet, which materials caused the bulb to light
7. Have students share their results; write the following terms on the board: insulator, conductor
8. Instruct students to determine which of their two groups would be insulators and which would be conductors; facilitate an appropriate discussion to reinforce the concepts.
9. Challenge students to list other items in the room that would be either insulators or conductors.
10. Have students identify 10 additional materials to test; following predictions about the ability of the bulb to light, have students conduct their test, listing what materials are insulators and those that are conductors.
11. Following the sharing of results, have students brainstorm where insulators and conductors are used in the real world and why.

PUTTING IT TO THE TEST
Student Sheet

Make a circuit with a battery, bulb and two wires. Leave the ends of the wires free. Select an object or material, then touch it to both wires. Observe to see if the bulb lights or not. Sort your collection of materials into two groups based on your observations; develop a title for each group.

What do you think is the main difference between the two different types of materials?

How does this affect the ability of the light bulb to light or not light?

Based on your knowledge of circuits, what would you call each group?

Spider Circuits
Engineering a Spider

Time Required: 45-60 minutes

How this learning experience meets the national science education standards:

Content Standard A: Science as Inquiry: As a result of activities in grades 5-8, all students should develop:

Abilities necessary to do scientific inquiry
- Identify questions that can be answered through scientific investigations.
- Design and conduct a scientific investigation.
- Use appropriate tools and techniques to gather, analyze and interpret data.
- Develop descriptions, explanations, predictions and models using evidence.
- Think critically and logically to make the relationships between evidence and explanations.
- Recognize and analyze alternative explanations and predictions.
- Communicate scientific procedures and explanations.
- Use mathematics in all aspects of scientific inquiry.

Understanding Scientific Inquiry
- Different kinds of questions suggest different kinds of scientific investigations.
- Current scientific knowledge and understanding guide scientific investigations.
- Mathematics is important in all aspects of scientific inquiry.
- Technology used to gather data enhances accuracy and allows scientists to analyze and quantify results of investigations.
- Scientific explanations emphasize evidence, have logically consistent arguments, and use scientific principles, models and theories.
- Science advances through legitimate skepticism.
- Scientific investigations sometimes result in new ideas and phenomena for study, generate new methods or procedures for an investigation, or develop new technologies to improve the collection of data.

Content Standard B: As a result of their activities in grades 5-8, all students should develop an understanding of:

Transfer of Energy
- Energy is a property of many substances and is associated with heat, light, electricity, mechanical motion, sound, nuclei, and the nature of a chemical. Energy is transferred in many ways.
- Light interacts with matter by transmission (including refraction), absorption, or scattering (including reflection). To see an object, light from that object--emitted by or scattered from it--must enter the eye.
- Electrical circuits provide a means of transferring electrical energy when heat, light, sound, and chemical changes are produced.

163

- In most chemical and nuclear reactions, energy is transferred into or out of a system. Heat, light, mechanical motion, or electricity might all be involved in such transfers.

Content Standard E: Science and Technology: As a result of activities in grades 5-8, a students should develop:

Understanding about science and technology
- Scientific inquiry and technological design have similarities and differences. Scientists propose explanations for questions about the natural world, and engineers propose solutions relating to human problems, needs, and aspirations. Technological solutions are temporary; technologies exist within nature and so they cannot contravene physical or biological principles; technological solutions have side effects; and technologies cost, carry risks, and provide benefits.
- Science and technology are reciprocal. Science helps drive technology, as it addresses questions that demand more sophisticated instruments and provides principles for better instrumentation and technique. Technology is essential to science, because it provides instruments and techniques that enable observations of objects and phenomena that are otherwise unobservable due to factors such as quantity, distance, location, size, and speed. Technology also provides tools for investigations, inquiry, and analysis.
- Perfectly designed solutions do not exist. All technological solutions have trade-offs, such as safety, cost, efficiency, and appearance. Engineers often build in back-up systems to provide safety. Risk is part of living in a highly technological world. Reducing risk often results in new technology.
- Technological designs have constraints. Some constraints are unavoidable, for example, properties of materials, or effects of weather and friction; other constraints limit choices in the design, for example, environmental protection, human safety, and aesthetics.
- Technological solutions have intended benefits and unintended consequences. Some consequences can be predicted, others cannot.

How this learning experience meets the National Standards for Technological Literacy:
- Standard 1. Students will develop an understanding of the characteristics and scope of technology.
- Standard 2. Students will develop an understanding of the core concepts of technology.
- Standard 3. Students will develop an understanding of the relationships among technologies and the connections between technology and other fields of study.
- Standard 10. Students will develop an understanding of the role of troubleshooting, research and development, invention and innovation, and experimentation in problem solving.

Overview:

Students will learn that electricity will only flow to light up a bulb if the circuit is complete. With broken circuits, the bulb will not light.

Background:

- Conductors are materials which allow electrical current to flow through a material.
- Insulators are materials which stop the flow of electrical current.

Teacher Notes:

It may be helpful for students to draw their Spider Circuit while working with it, in order to correctly identify which legs work successfully together; scratch paper may be needed for this.

When making the Spider Circuit, be certain that the legs are secured inside the container so that if you touch one leg, it's opposing leg won't automatically move and give away the solution to the puzzle. It may also be helpful to number or place letters beside each leg in order for students to more accurately identify the legs when recording their data. If you plan for the students to be able to look inside the Spider Circuit when they are finished with the test, do not glue the top to the base after completing construction.

Safety Notes:

Students should be told to keep wires away from all electrical outlets. If students create a short circuit, the wires will become hot. Students should disconnect the batteries.

Getting Started:

1. Build the Spider Circuits as follows:
   - Obtain a round plastic container (Cool Whip containers work well)
   - Put eight holes evenly distributed around the base of the container, near the rim
   - Thread four pieces of wire through the holes so that each wire goes through two holes
   - Knot or tape the wires inside the container to keep them from slipping out of the holes
   - Put the lid back on the container and decorate it to look like a spider, if desired

2. Organize sets of materials with the following included:
   - 2 batteries
   - Bulb
   - Bulb holder
   - Several pieces of wire

3. Copy student sheets.

Materials Needed Per Pair of Students:

- 2 batteries
- Battery holder
- Bulb
- Bulb holder
- Several pieces of wire
- Student sheets
- Spider Circuit

Procedure:

1. Assemble students into cooperative groups; identify appropriate student pairs.
2. Present each pair of students with a battery, piece of wire, and bulb; ask them to make the bulb light.
3. Following successful tests, present the students with several more pieces of wire, another battery, a battery holder, and bulb holder.
4. Ask the students to place the bulb in the bulb holder, the batteries in the battery holder, and make the bulb light.
5. Discuss the student results as needed.
6. Show the students a Spider Circuit; inform them that they will be challenged to use the materials they have been working with to determine which pairs of "legs" go together to make the light bulb light up.
7. Have students share their results and compare experiences; facilitate a discussion that focuses on why only certain sets of "legs" would allow the bulb to light.

Spider Circuits
Student Sheet

Using the materials provided, determine which pairs of "legs" go together by causing the bulb to light up. Log your attempts and indicate your successful combinations. Sketch the inside of the spider to show which wires are connected.

Amplified Kazoo

urning Analog Sound into a
igital Masterpiece

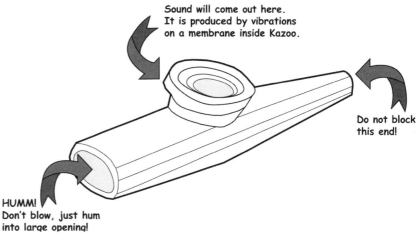

Sound will come out here.
It is produced by vibrations
on a membrane inside Kazoo.

Do not block
this end!

HUMM!
Don't blow, just hum
into large opening!

Time Required: 45-60 minutes

ow this learning experience meets the national science education
tandards:

ontent Standard A: Science as Inquiry: As a result of activities in grades 5-8, all
udents should develop:

bilities necessary to do scientific inquiry
- Identify questions that can be answered through scientific investigations.
- Design and conduct a scientific investigation.
- Use appropriate tools and techniques to gather, analyze and interpret data.
- Develop descriptions, explanations, predictions and models using evidence.
- Think critically and logically to make the relationships between evidence and explanations.
- Recognize and analyze alternative explanations and predictions.
- Communicate scientific procedures and explanations.
- Use mathematics in all aspects of scientific inquiry.

nderstanding Scientific Inquiry
- Different kinds of questions suggest different kinds of scientific investigations.
- Current scientific knowledge and understanding guide scientific investigations.
- Mathematics is important in all aspects of scientific inquiry.
- Technology used to gather data enhances accuracy and allows scientists to analyze and quantify results of investigations.
- Scientific explanations emphasize evidence, have logically consistent arguments, and use scientific principles, models and theories.
- Science advances through legitimate skepticism.
- Scientific investigations sometimes result in new ideas and phenomena for study, generate new methods or procedures for an investigation, or develop new technologies to improve the collection of data.

ontent Standard B: As a result of their activities in grades 5-8, all students should
evelop an understanding of:

ransfer of Energy
- Energy is a property of many substances and is associated with heat, light, electricity, mechanical motion, sound, nuclei, and the nature of a chemical. Energy is transferred in many ways.

- Light interacts with matter by transmission (including refraction), absorption, or scattering (including reflection). To see an object, light from that object--emitted by or scattered from it--must enter the eye
- Electrical circuits provide a means of transferring electrical energy when heat, light, sound, and chemical changes are produced.
- In most chemical and nuclear reactions, energy is transferred into or out of a system. Heat, light, mechanical motion, or electricity might all be involved in such transfers.

Content Standard E: Science and Technology: As a result of activities in grades 5-8, a students should develop:

Abilities of technological design
- Identify appropriate problems for technological design.
- Design a solution or a product.
- Implement a proposed design.
- Evaluate completed technological designs or products.
- Communicate the process of technological design.

Understanding about science and technology
- Scientific inquiry and technological design have similarities and differences. Scientists propose explanations for questions about the natural world, and engineers propose solutions relating to human problems, needs, and aspirations. Technological solutions are temporary; technologies exist within nature and so they cannot contravene physical or biological principles; technological solutions have side effects; and technologies cost, carry risks, and provide benefits.
- Science and technology are reciprocal. Science helps drive technology, as it addresses questions that demand more sophisticated instruments and provides principles for better instrumentation and technique. Technology is essential to science, because it provides instruments and techniques that enable observations of objects and phenomena that are otherwise unobservable due to factors such as quantity, distance, location, size, and speed. Technology also provides tools for investigations, inquiry, and analysis.
- Perfectly designed solutions do not exist. All technological solutions have trade-offs, such as safety, cost efficiency, and appearance. Engineers often build in back-up systems to provide safety. Risk is part of living in a highly technological world. Reducing risk often results in new technology.
- Technological designs have constraints. Some constraints are unavoidable, for example, properties of materials, or effects of weather and friction; other constraints limit choices in the design, for example, environmental protection, human safety, and aesthetics.
- Technological solutions have intended benefits and unintended consequences. Some consequences can be predicted, others cannot.

How this learning experience meets the National Standards for Technological Literacy:
- Standard 1. Students will develop an understanding of the characteristics and scope of technology.
- Standard 2. Students will develop an understanding of the core concepts of technology.
- Standard 3. Students will develop an understanding of the relationships among technologies and the connections between technology and other fields of study.
- Standard 4. Students will develop an understanding of the cultural, social, economic, and political effects of technology
- Standard 5. Students will develop an understanding of the effects of technology on the environment.
- Standard 6. Students will develop an understanding of the role of society in the development and use of technology.
- Standard 8. Students will develop an understanding of the attributes of design.
- Standard 9. Students will develop an understanding of engineering design.
- Standard 10. Students will develop an understanding of the role of troubleshooting, research and development, invention and innovation, and experimentation in problem solving.

Overview:

Students will convert mechanical energy (analog sounds) into electrical energy (digital sounds) and thereby amplify a kazoo through a set of computer speakers.

Background:

The kazoo is in the family of musical instruments called, "mirlitons". When you hum or speak into the large opening, the sound of your voice causes the wax paper membrane to vibrate in the kazoo and cause a "nasal" sound. The shape of the kazoo helps amplify and project the sound. In addition, by covering or partially covering the hole on the far end, many different sounds can be created.

Piezo electric transducers are commonly used as speakers and convert mechanical vibrations into electrical energy. In this case, when a student hums into the kazoo, the sound produces a vibration in the membrane of the kazoo and the piezo electric transducer generates an electric potential (voltage) by converting the mechanical energy to electrical energy. The voltage generated is too small to power speakers or headphones. Therefore, computer speakers with their own power source are needed to hear the amplification of the kazoo.

Other energy conversion examples:
- Baseball hitting a baseball bat coverts mechanical energy to sound energy.
- Car tires rotating convert mechanical energy to heat energy (friction).
- Car engines convert chemical energy (gasoline) into heat and kinetic energy.
- Solar panels convert solar radiation (light and heat) into electrical energy.

Teacher Notes:

Students may work alone or in teams but each team should have only one designated kazoo player to limit the spread of germs.

Safety:

The tip of the soldering iron can reach 750 degrees! Be very careful!
- Keep the soldering iron away from any flammable materials.
- The on-indicator light shows when the iron is plugged in and hot. If the light is off, the iron may still be hot.
- To avoid burns, always assume the iron is hot and don't touch it.
- Be sure the tip of the iron does not come into contact with any electrical cords.
- Always work in a well-ventilated area.
- Safety goggles are recommended.
- After use, unplug the iron and allow it to cool.

Materials:

- Kazoo
- Piezo transducer (Radio shack # 273-073A)
- 1/8" mono phone jack (Radio Shack # 274-251)
- Soldering gun and solder
- Cool melt glue gun
- Glue stick
- Drill

- ⅛" or ¼" drill bit
- Computer speakers
- Safety goggles

Procedure:

1. Inside of the piezo transducer is a piezo mic that will serve as the amplification device for your kazoo. To make this work, you must extract the piezo mic (brass disc) from the piezo transducer by following the instructions below:

   - Locate the piezo transducer 273-073A.

   - Using pliers, break off the two plastic tabs on the sides of the casing. The two tabs are spaced 180 degrees apart from each other.

   - Using pliers, break the casing around the piezo mic. Be careful not to damage the input leads or the piezo disc.

   - Using a thin edged screwdriver, gently pry the back plate off of the casing without touching the brass piezo disk.

   - Once the back is off, break off the edges of the plastic casing so that you can pull out the piezo disc without breaking the leads. Always err on the side of caution when removing the disc as the leads can break-off easily.

2. The disc that you extracted is brass and should have two wires (leads) attached to it. Solder the two leads from the disc to the two connectors on the on the phone jack by following the directions below. Polarity is not important.

   - Soldering is the process of heating up metals so that you can join them together. There are many ways to join metals such as brazing and welding but soldering uses the lowest temperatures.

   - When you melt solder, the metal becomes a liquid and covers the components that you want to attach. This covering creates the electrically conductive junction that allows the electricity to flow through your circuit. An advantage of soldering is that if you ever want to take the circuit apart or wish to rewire it, the junction can be de-soldered simply by heating the connection and removing the solder.

   - Note: If the components are not clean, the liquid solder won't stick to them. If the components are not heated, the liquid solder won't stick to them.

   - Heat the end of the piezo wire and the phone jack connector by holding the tip of the soldering iron against both the connector and the wire. While holding the soldering iron in this position, place the end of the roll of solder at the junction of the wire and connector. Do not touch the solder to the tip of the soldering iron. Heat the wire and connector so that it becomes sufficiently hot enough to melt the solder. The solder will melt and flow onto the joint. Allow just enough solder to melt to cover it. Your solder joint should be shiny.

   - If solder is melted on the tip of iron instead of by heating the wire and connector, it is referred to as a "cold solder joint". Typically, this type of joint does not conduct electricity consistently. You can recognize it because it will look more like a ball of metal than a smooth and shiny connection.

   - When solder turns liquid and flows over the wire and connector, quickly slide the iron away to leave the joint neat. Excess heat on the connection can make the solder appear to evaporate. Blow on the joint to speed its cooling.

   - Hint: A small amount of fresh solder on the tip of the iron when you begin soldering will help to carry heat from the iron to the joint.

- Maintain your soldering iron by keeping a thin coating of solder on the end of the soldering iron tip when not in use to prevent oxidation.

3. Locate your kazoo and drill a $1/8$" or $1/4$" air hole in one side of the kazoo about $1/2$" from the kazoo opening at the top.
4. With the wires facing up, hold the piezo disc over the hole at the top of the kazoo (where the sound comes out) and test where to get the best sound. Move the disc around while playing. When you find the best spot, mark it and glue it onto the kazoo using a cool melt glue gun.
5. Glue the phone jack onto the kazoo about halfway between the piezo disc and the smaller opening.
6. Plug your computer speakers into the phone jack and hum a few bars. Note: Headphones don't work. You need a speaker that is powered by electricity to provide the amplification.

Troubleshooting:

If your kazoo doesn't amplify:

1. Make sure that you have good solder joints. If you use too much solder and connect two leads that should not be connected, place the tip of the soldering iron between the two leads to remove the excess solder.
2. Solder joints are not capable of taking a lot of stress or movement so be careful when moving the wires around.
3. Be careful not to block the small hole that you drilled in the side of the kazoo or the membrane inside will not be able to vibrate.
4. Be careful not to block the air flow of the small end of the kazoo.
5. Kazoo sounds are made by humming (do not blow) into the large opening on the horizontal axis.

Amplified Kazoo
Student Sheet

What does a piezoelectric transducer do? Why does it help amplify the kazoo?

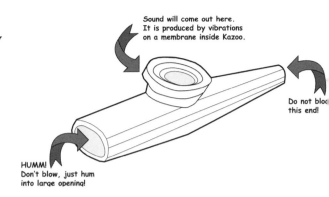

Sound will come out here. It is produced by vibrations on a membrane inside Kazoo.

Do not block this end!

HUMM! Don't blow, just hum into large opening!

Why is it important to not touch the solder to the soldering iron when soldering?

What are two examples of mechanical energy being converted to another form of energy?

What are two examples of another energy transformation?

Lunar Treasures

Exploring Inquiry and Design

Time Required: 60-90 minutes

How this learning experience meets the national science education standards:

Content Standard A: Science as Inquiry: As a result of activities in grades 5-8, all students should develop:

Abilities necessary to do scientific inquiry
- Identify questions that can be answered through scientific investigations.
- Design and conduct a scientific investigation.
- Use appropriate tools and techniques to gather, analyze and interpret data.
- Develop descriptions, explanations, predictions and models using evidence.
- Think critically and logically to make the relationships between evidence and explanations.
- Recognize and analyze alternative explanations and predictions.
- Communicate scientific procedures and explanations.
- Use mathematics in all aspects of scientific inquiry.

Understanding Scientific Inquiry
- Different kinds of questions suggest different kinds of scientific investigations.
- Current scientific knowledge and understanding guide scientific investigations.
- Mathematics is important in all aspects of scientific inquiry.
- Technology used to gather data enhances accuracy and allows scientists to analyze and quantify results of investigations.
- Scientific explanations emphasize evidence, have logically consistent arguments, and use scientific principles, models and theories.
- Science advances through legitimate skepticism.
- Scientific investigations sometimes result in new ideas and phenomena for study, generate new methods or procedures for an investigation, or develop new technologies to improve the collection of data.

Content Standard B: As a result of their activities in grades 5-8, all students should develop an understanding of:

Transfer of Energy
- Energy is a property of many substances and is associated with heat, light, electricity, mechanical motion, sound, nuclei, and the nature of a chemical. Energy is transferred in many ways.
- Light interacts with matter by transmission (including refraction), absorption, or scattering (including

reflection). To see an object, light from that object--emitted by or scattered from it--must enter the eye

- Electrical circuits provide a means of transferring electrical energy when heat, light, sound, and chemical changes are produced.
- In most chemical and nuclear reactions, energy is transferred into or out of a system. Heat, light, mechanical motion, or electricity might all be involved in such transfers.

Content Standard E: Science and Technology: As a result of activities in grades 5-8, a students should develop:

Abilities of technological design

- Identify appropriate problems for technological design.
- Design a solution or a product.
- Implement a proposed design.
- Evaluate completed technological designs or products.
- Communicate the process of technological design.

Understanding about science and technology

- Scientific inquiry and technological design have similarities and differences. Scientists propose explanations for questions about the natural world, and engineers propose solutions relating to human problems, needs, and aspirations. Technological solutions are temporary; technologies exist within nature and so they cannot contravene physical or biological principles; technological solutions have side effects; and technologies cost, carry risks, and provide benefits.
- Science and technology are reciprocal. Science helps drive technology, as it addresses questions that demand more sophisticated instruments and provides principles for better instrumentation and technique. Technology is essential to science, because it provides instruments and techniques that enable observations of objects and phenomena that are otherwise unobservable due to factors such as quantity, distance, location, size, and speed. Technology also provides tools for investigations, inquiry, and analysis.
- Perfectly designed solutions do not exist. All technological solutions have trade-offs, such as safety, cost efficiency, and appearance. Engineers often build in back-up systems to provide safety. Risk is part of living in a highly technological world. Reducing risk often results in new technology.
- Technological designs have constraints. Some constraints are unavoidable, for example, properties of materials, or effects of weather and friction; other constraints limit choices in the design, for example, environmental protection, human safety, and aesthetics.
- Technological solutions have intended benefits and unintended consequences. Some consequences can be predicted, others cannot.

How this learning experience meets the National Standards for Technological Literacy:

- Standard 1. Students will develop an understanding of the characteristics and scope of technology.
- Standard 2. Students will develop an understanding of the core concepts of technology.
- Standard 3. Students will develop an understanding of the relationships among technologies and the connections between technology and other fields of study.
- Standard 4. Students will develop an understanding of the cultural, social, economic, and political effects of technology
- Standard 5. Students will develop an understanding of the effects of technology on the environment.
- Standard 6. Students will develop an understanding of the role of society in the development and use of technology.
- Standard 8. Students will develop an understanding of the attributes of design.
- Standard 9. Students will develop an understanding of engineering design.
- Standard 10. Students will develop an understanding of the role of troubleshooting, research and development, invention and innovation, and experimentation in problem solving.

Overview:

In this project, students will build their own "Lunar Treasures" game from foamcore, wire, and basic electronic components, including a buzzer and an LED. In Challenge 1, they will set up the game board. In Challenge 2, they will make the electrical connections and try their hand at extracting the jewels without any damage!

Background:

Scenario - Newly confirmed energy jewels on the moon could help solve the energy crisis if harvesting can be made without damage to the jewels. The colored jewels were found inside the moon's craters and are very sensitive to damage. If students accidentally brush up against the sides of the crater during extraction, the jewels will be destroyed and rendered useless. To make matters worse, there are only six jewels and without all six, engineers cannot solve the energy crisis on earth!

Teacher Notes:

In the Lunar Treasures Game, students will place a jewel into each moon crater. They will then wire a pair of metal tweezers to the game board thus making it conductive. When performing the extraction, if students brush against the side of the moon crater and damage the jewel, the game buzzer will buzz and the LED will light showing their disqualification.

Safety:

Students will be using a jigsaw blade to cut holes in the their lunar surface. Exercise caution when using the blades.

Materials:

- Foam core (2 pieces. Top panel: 6"x10", Bottom panel: 6"x8")
- Moon Picture
- Machine Screws (3)
- Washers (5)
- Nuts (5)
- LEDs 2-Volt
- Resistor (390 ohm)
- Buzzer
- Black Wire (12 inches)
- Red wire (24 inches)
- Saw blade for cutting holes
- Battery pack and Batteries (4 AA)
- Foil
- Tweezers
- Jewels (6)
- Glue Stick
- Wire Stripper
- Ruler
- Screwdriver

Procedure:

The top panel for your game is a rectangular piece of foam core, measuring about 6 inches by 10 inches. ***NOTE: The size of the top panel is the same width as the lunar image, but 2 inches longer.***

Challenge 1: Construct the Game Board

The Lunar Treasures game is built from two layers of foam core. The top layer has aluminum foil under the image of the moon while the bottom layer is covered in aluminum foil. The aluminum foil is part of the game's electronic circuit, which you wire together in Challenge 2.

Applying the Lunar Image

The lunar image should be secured to the top panel with glue from a glue stick. It is important to align the image properly, so have students pay close attention when gluing it down.

1. Locate the longer piece of foam core. Align the right side of the image to the right side of your panel. *NOTE: There should be about two inches of uncovered space on the panel to the left of the image.* Tape your image to the foam core.

2. Trace an outline of the buzzer on the center of the panel area to the left of the lunar image. The outline should be tight and precise so that the buzzer will fit snugly in the opening.

3. Mark a small circular opening, about ½" in diameter, on the top left side of the lunar image.

4. Using a screwdriver or your tweezers, make a hole in the center of each crator large enough to insert your jigsaw blade. Using the jigsaw blade, cut out each crator. Do the same to cut out the rectangle for the buzzer. *NOTE: Be very careful not to cut outside the crator and not to cut your finger!*

5. Carefully remove the tape from the image and place the image to the side.

6. Apply a thin layer of glue to the top side of the panel. Be sure to cover the entire surface evenly but do not apply glue to the left-most two inches of the panel.

7. Cut the foil the same size as the smaller piece of foam core. Press the foil into place onto the larger piece of foam core (aligned to the right side of the foamcore). This will cover the holes you just made.

8. Apply a thin layer of glue to the backside of the image. Be sure to cover the entire surface evenly.

9. Place the lunar image in exactly the same place you had it before. Align the patient image holes over the holes in the foam core. Press the image into place onto the top of the foil. *NOTE: There should be about two inches of uncovered space on the left side of the panel.*

Adding the Bottom Panel

The game's bottom panel (smaller piece of foam core) provides backing for your patient's operation sites. It is wrapped in foil, so that it can conduct electricity to other components in the game's circuit.

1. Wrap your bottom panel in a smooth layer of aluminum foil. Glue the foil in place.

2. Test fit your bottom panel to make sure that it provides backing for all of your lunar crator openings. NOTE: The bottom panel should also be visible in the hole for the battery lead.

3. Glue the top panel to the bottom panel.

4. Reach inside each operation point and pierce the center of the foil with a pen or pencil. Press the foil onto the sides of the holes you cut into the top foam core piece. Note: The foil on the sides of the holes needs to touch the foil on the bottom of the cavities to make a connection.

About Conductors, Insulators, and Resistors

Aluminum and other metals are very good at carrying electricity in circuits; these materials are known as conductors. Other materials do not carry electricity very well at all; these materials are known as insulators. Good insulators include certain types of plastic and rubber. The power cords for household electrical appliances, such as lamps and fans, have a conductor inside (usually copper) that is coated with a plastic insulator. This way electricity can flow through the cord, but it cannot escape from the circuit if the cord comes in contact with another conductor (like your hand!)

Challenge 2: Build the Game Circuit

The circuit for the Lunar Treasure game is fairly simple. The red lead from the battery is connected to the foil-wrapped bottom layer. If a player touches the foil with the tweezers, it completes a circuit that includes the buzzer and the LED.

Adding the Buzzer and Terminals

Three machine screws provide points of connection for the game's electronic components. These should be positioned on either side of the buzzer, and in the circular opening hole for the battery leads (top left corner of the lunar image).

1. Press fit the buzzer into the rectangular opening in the game's top panel, tape in place if necessary.

2. Using a screwdriver or your tweezers, add the three machine screws, securing each with a washer on top and a nut on the bottom. One of the screws should fit inside the circular opening you made on the top left corner of the lunar image. The other two screws should be placed below on either side of the buzzer.

Adding the LED

In your game, you will place an LED on your game board in any place that will insure it will **not** come in contact with the foil. It will light if your hand slips during extraction and the jewel is damaged.

1. Using a screwdriver or your tweezers, make a small puncture in the top panel where you want to position the LED. NOTE: The LED must not touch the foil-wrapped bottom panel.

2. Push the LED's pins through the top panel, and bend them apart slightly to secure the LED in place.

About Parallel and Series Circuits

Whenever two components are included into the same circuit, there are two different ways they can be wired: in series or in parallel. The picture to the right shows the difference between these two types of circuits.

Series circuit (left) and parallel circuit (right).

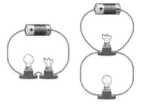

Broken series circuit (left) and parallel circuit (right).

In the series circuit, both components are connected in a row, with electricity passing first through one then the other. In the parallel circuit, electricity passes through both components at the same time. A major advantage of parallel circuits is that if one component malfunctions, the other continues to function. In a series circuit, when one component breaks, both components stop working.

Wiring the Battery Pack and Buzzer

The red and black leads from the battery pack and the buzzer connect to the machine screws that you added in the last step.

1. Connect the red battery lead to the machine screw that comes through the foil-wrapped bottom layer on the top left of the lunar image.

2. Connect the black battery lead and the black buzzer wire to the machine screw in the board's upper-left corner (above the buzzer).

3. Connect the red battery lead to the remaining machine screw.

Wiring the LED

Before connecting the LED, be sure that you know which pin is the power pin, and which is the ground pin. The positive side of the LED is longer (connect to the red wire).

1. Connect the short length of black wire to the machine screw terminal above the buzzer. Connect 8-inches of the red wire to the terminal below the buzzer.

2. Twist together one end of the 390-Ohm resistor with the loose end of the red wire, and twist together the other end of the resistor with the LED's power pin.

3. Twist together the loose end of the black wire with the LED's ground pin.

Connecting the Tweezers

Using the remaining length of insulated red wire, connect the tweezers to the machine screw below the buzzer (red side) on the front side of the game's top panel.

1. Connect one end of the red wire to the machine screw.

2. Connect the other end of the red wire to the base of the tweezers. Wrap the wire to the base and tape into place if necessary.

Inserting Game Pieces and Playing the Game

1. Insert a jewel into each crator.

2. Move the power switch on your battery pack to the ON position (if applicable).

3. Try to retrieve the jewels from the lunar surface. If you accidentally touch the side of the crator, the buzzer should sound and the LED should light.

4. If either the buzzer does not sound or the LED doesn't light, check your circuitry and adjust as needed.

Lunar Treasure Game Image

The lunar image below should be cut out and secured to the top panel (longer panel) with glue from a glue stick. Align the right side of the image to the right side of your panel. It is important to align the image properly, so pay close attention when gluing it down. *NOTE: There should be about 2 inches of uncovered space on the panel to the left of the image.*

Lunar Treasure Game
Student Sheet

1. Give three examples of a conductor.

   1. _____

   2. _____

   3. _____

2. Give three examples of insulators.

   1. _____

   2. _____

   3. _____

3. Would plastic wrap work instead of foil? Why or why not?

4. What is the advantage of purchasing holiday lights that are strung in parallel?

Electrical Engineering Crossword Puzzle

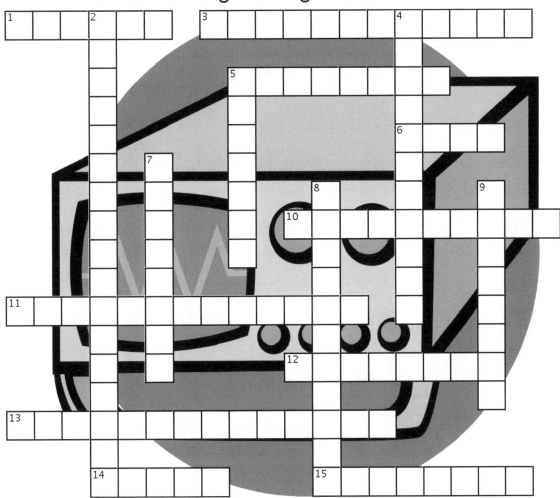

Across

1. Medical doctors use _____ to cut out cancerous growths.
3. A technician may use the schematic to test the circuit's _____.
5. Electricity can be created from _____ sources.
6. The Institute of Electrical and Electronic Engineering
10. The developments of electrical and _____ engineers are everywhere.
11. _____ repair equipment.
12. Flashlights are _____ light sources we can carry around.
13. Communications is a _____ within electrical engineering.
14. Fiber optics utilize the properties of _____.
15. The federal government hires technologists and technicians to maintain national _____ equipment.

Down

2. A robot is considered an _____ device.
4. Electrical engineers are _____ problem solvers who enjoy challenges.
5. Conductors are materials which allow electrical _____ to flow.
7. Two to four engineers designing a product.
8. Cell phones contain _____.
9. Electrical engineers helped invent the _____.

Electrical Engineering Crossword Puzzle

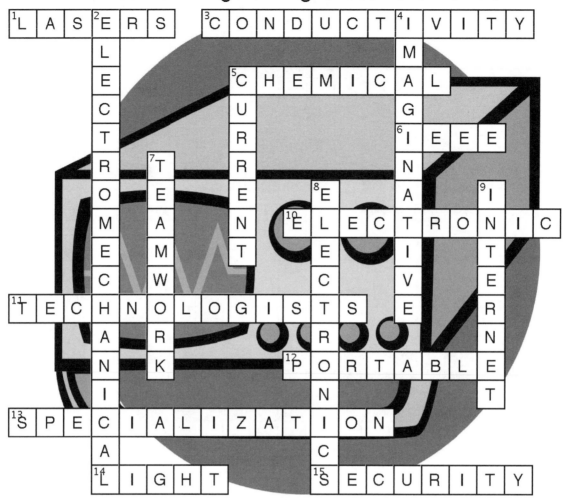

The completed crossword grid reads:

Across: 1. LASERS 3. CONDUCTIVITY 5. CHEMICAL 6. IEEE 10. ELECTRONIC 11. TECHNOLOGISTS 12. PORTABLE 13. SPECIALIZATION 14. LIGHT 15. SECURITY

Down: 2. ELECTROMECHANIC 4. IMAGINATIVE 5. CURRENT 7. TEAMWORK 8. ELECTRONICS 9. INTERNET

Across

1. Medical doctors use _____ to cut out cancerous growths. [lasers]
3. A technician may use the schematic to test the circuit's _____. [conductivity]
5. Electricity can be created from _____ sources. [chemical]
6. The Institute of Electrical and Electronic Engineering [IEEE]
10. The developments of electrical and _____ engineers are everywhere. [electronic]
11. _____ repair equipment. [Technologists]
12. Flashlights are _____ light sources we can carry around. [portable]
13. Communications is a _____ within electrical engineering. [specialization]
14. Fiber optics utilize the properties of _____. [light]
15. The federal government hires technologists and technicians to maintain national _____ equipment. [security]

Down

2. A robot is considered an _____ device. [electromechanical]
4. Electrical engineers are _____ problem solvers who enjoy challenges. [imaginative]
5. Conductors are materials which allow electrical _____ to flow. [current]
7. Two to four engineers designing a product. [teamwork]
8. Cell phones contain _____. [electronics]
9. Electrical engineers helped invent the _____. [Internet]

Electrical Engineering
Wordsearch Puzzle

```
L P F D R E O V O X J C U Z Y A U Q G S E Z U V O
A C Y W R Z H C H E M I C A L M E I P L Y P E R V
C B U O M O Y A M O P T N F C W G E S S S S Z P W
I Y X E L E C T R O N I C S O E C H X Z T E J Y C
N I A H C A O M H W B X I I H I O I E S X G F C I
A Y B K V B G X W O D V B V A D C V I I G R I L N
H A R C U R R E N T J U R L E O K G Z A N T I E O
C E T J X T H G I L O M I P N V O R R M A S L O R
E E A S J X J E H M C Z S D I L I X O X I B R F T
M E L X K N S P W P A X U N O S Z T B W A J G N C
O I X I S R I Z J T N C T N B E D S A T M D B B E
R L K J E K E C I P T E H K M C S Y R N E A E U L
T X N S R W A O D I R C O V X U V O W B I T E T E
C F A W S Q N Y V N E J C P W R P U J U J G N T D
E L N J N J D I E T G U N W H I J V Z P G N A G L
L H M U S A T T W U V M J F Q T V N E D Y P L M E
E I J E L Y T S B P G J S B X Y C P X B R V I K I
```

1. A robot is considered an _____ device.

3. Cell phones contain _____.

5. _____ repair equipment.

7. Electrical engineers helped invent the _____.

9. Electricity can be created from _____ sources.

11. Conductors are materials which allow electrical _____ to flow.

13. The Institute of Electrical and Electronic Engineering

15. Medical doctors use _____ to cut out cancerous growths.

2. Communications is a _____ within electrical engineering.

4. The developments of electrical and _____ engineers are everywhere.

6. Electrical engineers are _____ problem solvers who enjoy challenges.

8. A technician may use the schematic to test the circuit's _____.

10. The federal government hires technologists and technicians to maintain national _____ equipment.

12. Flashlights are _____ light sources we can carry around.

14. Two to four engineers designing a product.

16. Fiber optics utilize the properties of _____.

Electrical Engineering
Wordsearch Puzzle

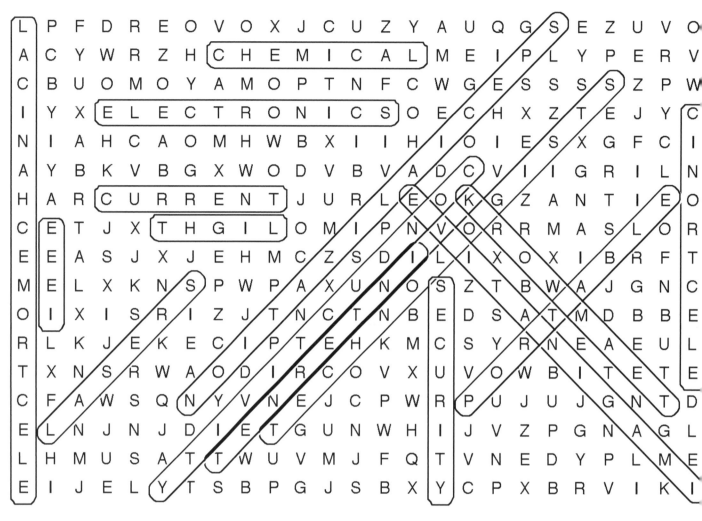

1. A robot is considered an _____ device. [electromechanical]
3. Cell phones contain _____. [electronics]

5. _____ repair equipment. [Technologists]

7. Electrical engineers helped invent the _____. [Internet]
9. Electricity can be created from _____ sources. [chemical]

11. Conductors are materials which allow electrical _____ to flow. [current]
13. The Institute of Electrical and Electronic Engineering [IEEE]
15. Medical doctors use _____ to cut out cancerous growths. [lasers]

2. Communications is a _____ within electrical engineering. [specialization]
4. The developments of electrical and _____ engineers are everywhere. [electronic]
6. Electrical engineers are _____ problem solvers who enjoy challenges. [imaginative]
8. A technician may use the schematic to test the circuit's _____. [conductivity]
10. The federal government hires technologists and technicians to maintain national _____ equipment. [security]
12. Flashlights are _____ light sources we can carry around. [portable]
14. Two to four engineers designing a product. [teamwork]
16. Fiber optics utilize the properties of _____. [light]

Resources - Engineering Education and Career Websites

Teaching Engineering

    Engineering Education Service Center - www.engineeringedu.com
    Teach Engineering - www.teachengineering.org
    Try Engineering - www.tryengineering.org
    Engineering Go for It - www.egfi-k12.org
    Engneer Your Life - engineeryourlife.org

Programs, Initiatives & Classroom Curricula

    AP (Advanced Placement Programs) - www.collegeboard.com/student/testing/ap/about.html
    Amatrol: integrated technical learning systems - www.amatrol.com
    Autodesk Design Academy - usa.autodesk.com/adsk/servlet/index?siteID=123112&id=3268568
    CEEO (Center for Engineering Educational Outreach), Tufts University - www.ceeo.tufts.edu
    Infinity Project - www.infinity-project.org
    Intel Innovation in Education - www97.intel.com/education
    JASON Foundation for Education - www.jasonproject.org/home.htm
    PLTW (Project Lead the Way) - www.pltw.org
    SEEK-16 (Strategies for Engineering Education K-16 Summit) - http://www.howardcc.edu/seek-16
    Design and Discovery - www97.intel.com/discover/DesignDiscovery/DD_Research/
    EXITE (EXploring Interests in Technology and Engineering, IBM) - www.ibm.com/ibm/ibmgives/grant/education/camp.shtml
    Intel NWSE (Northwest Science Expo)/ISEF (International Science & Engineering Fair) - www.nwse.org/
    MESA (Mathematics, Engineering, Science Achievement) - mesa.ucop.edu/home.html
    STARBASE (Science and Technology Academies Reinforcing Basic Aviation and Space Exploration) - starbasedod.org
    Techno Science Supersite - www.technosciencesupersite.org
    Youth Exploring Science - YES - www.youthexploringscience.org

Programs & Initiatives, Co-curricular, National

    American Society of Mechanical Engineers Diversity Outreach - www.asme.org/communities/diversities/bdo
    Discover Engineering - www.discoverengineering.org
    Dream It. Do It. Campaign - www.dreamit-doit.com
    FIRST (For Inspiration and Recognition of Science and Technology) - www.usfirst.org
    Girl Power 21st Century - www.celt.sunysb.edu/gp21
    Girls Go Tech - www.girlsgotech.org
    Girls Research Our World - www.ksu.edu/grow
    Graduates Linking with Undergraduates in Engineering (GLUE) at UT Austin - www.engr.utexas.edu/wep/glue
    Lemelson-MIT InvenTeams - web.mit.edu/inventeams
    MATHCOUNTS - www.mathcounts.org
    National Engineers Week - www.eweek.org
    PNNL (Pacific Northwest National Lab) Science and Engineering Education - science-ed.pnl.gov
    TexPREP & SAPREP (The Texas Pre-freshman Engineering Program) - www.prep-usa.org/portal/saprep
    Women in Engineering Proactive Network - www.wepan.org

Organizations

ASEE (American Society for Engineering Education) - www.asee.org
Advanced Technology Education Centers - www.atecenters.org
BEC (Business Education Compact) - becpdx.org
CIESE (Center for Innovation in Engineering and Science Education) - k12science.ati.stevens-tech.edu
EESC (Engineering Education Service Center) - www.engineeringedu.com
EPICS (Engineering Projects in Community Service) - epicsnational.ecn.purdue.edu
Future Scientists and Engineers of America - www.fsea.org
IEEE (Institute of Electrical and Electronics Engineers) - www.ieee.org/portal/sitel
ITEEA (International Technology and Engineering Education Association) - www.iteaconnect.org
NACME (National Action Council for Minorities in Engineering) - www.nacme.org
NSBE (National Society of Black Engineers) - www.nsbe.org
NSTA (National Science Teachers Association) - www.nsta.org
NWREL (Northwest Regional Education Laboratory) - www.nwrel.org
OACTE (Oregon Association of Career and Technical Educators) - www.oregonacte.org
OMSI - Oregon Museum of Science and Industry - www.omsi.edu
PAVTEC - www.pcc.edu/pavtec
RISE (Resources for Involving Scientists in Education) - www.nationalacademies.org/rise
SECME, Inc - www.promorphus.com/secme/index.ph
SEMI High Tech U - www.semi.org/foundation
SHPE (Society of Hispanic Professional Engineers) - www.shpe.org
TEO (Technology Educators of Oregon) - www.teoregon.com

Celeste Baine is a biomedical engineer, director of the Engineering Education Service Center and the award-winning author of over twenty books and booklets on engineering careers and education. She won the Norm Augustine Award from the National Academy of Engineering (The Norm Augustine award is given to an engineer who has demonstrated the capacity for communicating the excitement and wonder of engineering); the American Society for Engineering Education's Engineering Dean Council's Award for the Promotion of Engineering Education and Careers; and is listed on the National Engineers Week website as one of 50 engineers you should meet. The National Academy of Engineering has included Celeste in their Gallery of Women Engineers and she has been named one of the Nifty-Fifty individuals who have made a major impact on the field of engineering by the USA Science and Engineering Festival.

Cathi Cox-Boniol, currently ACHIEVE Coordinator for Lincoln Parish Schools, left a 17 year career at Choudrant High School in 1998 to become the Site Coordinator for Louisiana Tech University's Project LIFE. While at Louisiana Tech, she moved into the Program Coordinator position for CATALyST, the university's Center for Applied Teaching and Learning to Yield Scientific Thinking. Now forging community based partnerships through Lincoln ACHIEVE, Cox-Boniol has initiated both the STEM Satellite and STEM Seed magnet programs as well as a creative writing emphasis in partnership with Louisiana Tech and Grambling State Universities. Beginning in the fall of 2010 she also assumed the role of Director for New Tech @ Ruston, a 21st Century teaching and learning program. An instructor of online learning for PBS, her pursuit of educational excellence for all students has garnered Cox-Boniol numerous awards and honors.

Elizabeth Parry is a consultant in K-12 STEM (Science, Technology, Engineering and Mathematics) Curriculum and Professional Development and the director of K-16 STEM Partnership Development at the College of Engineering at North Carolina State University. For the past fifteen years, she has worked extensively with students from kindergarten to graduate school, parents and pre-service and in service teachers to both educate and excite them about engineering. She is an active member in the American Society for Engineering Education and currently serves as the chair-elect of the K-12 division. She has written numerous papers and speaks frequently to groups on STEM issues and the inclusion of engineering in K-12 education.

Engineering Education and Career Publications

Teaching Engineering Made Easy: A Friendly Introduction to Engineering Activities for Middle School Teachers (2nd Edition) - Includes Chemical, Civil and Mechanical Engineering Activities. $34.95

Is There an Engineer Inside You?: A Comprehensive Guide to Career Decisions in Engineering (Fourth Edition). $24.95

The Green Engineer: Engineering Careers to Save the Earth. $17.95

The Maritime Engineer: Careers in Naval Architecture and Marine, Ocean and Naval Engineering. $17.95

Engineers Make a Difference: Motivating Students to Pursue an Engineering Education. $21.95

The Musical Engineer: A Music Enthusiast's Guide to Engineering and Technology Careers. $17.95

The Fantastical Engineer: A Thrillseeker's Guide to Careers in Theme Park Engineering. $17.95

High Tech Hot Shots: Careers in Sports Engineering. $19.95

Ideas in Action: A Girl's Guide to Careers in Engineering. $7.95

DVDs

Engineers Can Do Anything: An Inspirational Guide into the World of Engineering Careers. 20 minutes. $24.95

Women in Engineering: The Best Kept Secret to Changing the World. 29 minutes. $29.95

The Road Ahead: Choosing an Engineering School. 14 Minutes. $14.95

**To Order:
call 1-541-988-1005 tel, Fax orders to 1-541-988-1008
Online orders www.engineeringedu.com**